630

20'

· County |

The Farm and the Village

by the same author

*

ASK THE FELLOWS WHO CUT THE HAY

THE PATTERN UNDER THE PLOUGH
Aspects of the Folk-Life of East Anglia

THE HORSE IN THE FURROW

The Farm and the Village

GEORGE EWART EVANS

with drawings by R. C. Lambeth

FABER AND FABER LIMITED

London: 24 Russell Square

First published in 1969
by Faber and Faber Limited
24 Russell Square, London W.C.1
Printed in Great Britain by
Ebenezer Baylis and Son, Limited
The Trinity Press, Worcester, and London

SBN 571 08804 x

To
Mary and Susan

Contents

Illustrations

PLATES

Illustrations

LINE DRAWINGS

Introduction

Before we can fully understand the history of a region like East Anglia, and even the changes that are going on at the present time, we must have a fair grasp of the history of its farming. This is the main thought behind this book. We can be sure that man has cultivated the soil of this region, by one method or another, for at least 4,000 years; and we know that the region, like the whole of south-eastern England, specialized in the growing of corn from early historical times.

Now farming is not something that is practised at the edge of society. It is central to its very being. This is an obvious truth when we think back to earlier times. Farming then was man's essential mode of life. He farmed to live, and his living was almost entirely farming: the cultivation of the soil and the tending of his beasts. But it is also true to say that farming has been the chief activity in this region throughout the historical period right up to the recent past of sixty or seventy years ago. Moreover the main line of farming in East Anglia has been of a particular kind: arable farming, the growing and the harvesting of crops. East Anglia, with its position on the east side of Britain and its consequent low rainfall, with its chalky soil and rich boulder-clays, is in fact ideal for the growing of corn.

In this connection it is useful to contrast the region with the wetter side of Britain, Wales or Ireland. There the main line in farming has always been pastoral, the grazing and tending of

Introduction

animals. The mild, wet climate is most suitable for the growing of grass. A young boy who recently went from East Anglia to Wales for a fortnight's summer holiday noticed, in that short time, the vital difference between his home county and the west. When he came back he told his parents: 'Wales is a funny country. All the fields are green.' Besides passing on a sharp piece of observation which many of his elders have failed to make, the boy had unwittingly hinted at the distinction between two separate cultures or societies many of whose differences can be traced to the different methods of winning a living from the soil. For the arable farming year has a different rhythm from the pastoral; and the atmosphere and even the physical structure of the villages in the arable areas is not the same as in those areas where grass is the main crop taken from the land.

It is suggested, therefore, that it is profitable to study a particular kind of farming not only for itself but because it affects the way of life of the country or region where it is practised. If this is true it should also be profitable to study the history of farming not by itself but against the background of the society which it nourished. This is what I have tried to do in the present book, and this is the reason I have called it *The Farm and the Village*.

Some of the book's chapters are concerned with the great changes that have taken place in the farming and the village since the coming of modern machinery. In addition to the obvious consequences to farming itself, this had one result which is important for our purpose. During the last half century or so the machines have displaced processes and customs that had been followed in more-or-less unaltered form since farming began. Thus the generation of men and women who last practised the old techniques became in their own life-time living archives or documents that are able to teach us the details of farming and a way of life in the village that had its roots in a long past.

For, owing to the relatively unchanging rhythm of farming during the whole of the time prior to modern mechanization,

14

the memories of these old people have much greater importance than is indicated by their own particular life-span. To put it in another way: their experience on the farm during their boyhood days was not much different from that of a boy who lived on the same farm during, for instance, the fourteenth century. This generation of country people has been one of the main sources of the information in this book; and I make no apology for going to them as reliable historical witnesses. I have often found them more accurate than the printed word, and certainly wider in their sympathies and infinitely more stimulating in their responses.

I have not tried to give a comprehensive account of the farming of East Anglia. So much information packed into so small a space would be misleading and probably unreadable. Instead I have tried to follow the main line of farming and to suggest its active links with the society of the region. It is hoped that what is read here will be a stimulus to further reading in books which deal more fully with farming's various aspects. I have frequently quoted from three of my own books about the region; and where I have been able to gather fresh illustrations of the topics discussed I have done so. Occasionally, however, I have repeated a paragraph or a story which I considered particularly apt. I hope the reader who has come across the passage before will overlook the repetition. The words repeated are not my own and are in my view well able to stand the test of inclusion in another setting.

Helmingham, February, 1968

Early Farmers: An Experiment

Most scholars believe that man first started to cultivate the soil in Britain during Neolithic times, from about 2,500 B.C. onwards. Before this period he was a hunter and food gatherer, living on animal flesh and the fruit, roots, and berries he could collect over a certain area. From a hunter of wild animals and a food-gatherer he progressed to the stage where it was possible to live off animals by controlling them to a certain degree, and by guiding them to the places where he knew there was good grazing. Animals like sheep, horses, goats, camels, reindeer were among the first to be domesticated; and we can get a fair idea how man lived at this second stage by studying how the tribes of the Old Testament lived on their sheep, the Scythians on their horses, or—in more recent times—the Eskimoes on their reindeer.

During this time, so is the theory, he had discovered that after a grassland had been burned the grasses came up more abundantly and gave more food for the animals. Early man must also have noticed that the actual seeds of the grasses were bigger and more abundant on the ash-strewn soil left after burning a tract of vegetation. Scholars infer that it is probable that the wild ancestors of wheat and barley were first grown in Western Iran after the seeds had been accidentally blown on to an area that had been purposefully burned off by the nomads to obtain better grass for their herds. Primitive man recognized the advantage of burning, and the increase of food that could thus be obtained. In this way the first method of true cultivation was born: cutting down scrub or forest and then burning the trees and vegetation and sowing seed in the resulting ash.

A Danish botanist, Johannes Iversen, proved about thirty years ago by experiments he made with the analysis of pollen in a Seland bog that this *slash-and-burn* theory, as it was called, was a true account of what actually happened. He had found layers of charcoal in the bog, and he satisfied himself by analysing the pollen which was still in the peat that the layers of charcoal were not due to chance burning of the scrub or forest but were caused by purposive slashing and burning. They were in fact early man's first method of making a seed-bed.

But Iversen and his colleague, Axel Steensberg, decided, nevertheless, to put this theory to the acid test of practice—to actual experiment. Therefore, with a group of scientists and archaeologists mainly from the Danish National Museum, they got permission to clear two acres of woodland by burning. A forest in South Jutland was chosen because it was of mixed oak, exactly the sort of forest in these latitudes that Neolithic man had to clear. But to control their test not all the forest was burned: part of it was simply cleared.

They proceeded to reproduce, as far as possible, the conditions under which primitive man worked. They obtained Neolithic axes from the museum; and reconstructed a wooden haft or handle, using as a model an actual haft that had been dug from a Danish bog. They began their experiment in February, 1952; and within five minutes of starting they had a disastrous set-back. All three stone axes were broken, and the haft had been split through after too hard a blow. But the first test, although disastrous, had told them something: flint axes are particularly fragile in frosty weather, and the wooden haft must not be tied too tightly to the flint head; the technique the Neolithic farmer must have used in chopping down trees was to chip at the trunk with short, rapid strokes of the axe using only the wrist and the elbow. By putting the whole weight of the shoulder behind their strokes, as they would with a modern steel axe, the archaeologists had soon shattered the haft and the three axes.

Having learned all this, two archaeologists of the party, using a flint axe that had not been sharpened since Neolithic times, were able after a little practice to cut down oak trees more than a foot in diameter within half an hour. In this way they felled the trees in the chosen area; but they did not try cutting down the bigger oaks: they killed these by cutting rings through the sap-wood. They were now compelled to leave the trees for a year to dry before they could burn them effectively.

After successfully igniting the area of fallen trees they had decided to clear by burning they were ready to sow the seed. But their choice of seed shows how carefully the experiment had been carried out. Iversen and Steensberg knew from finds of charred corn on archaeological sites in Denmark and from the impression of grain in pottery dug from the same sites that Neolithic man made use of three kinds of wheat: small spelt, emmer, and club-wheat. The barley he used was of the type with six rows, usually known as 'naked barley'. These primitive types of corn were still to be obtained from experimental corn-growing centres; and they decided to use these types of grain for their sowing.

But how were they going to sow on the ash left by the burning? They experimented chiefly with two methods: sowing broadcast, and using a digging-stick that made a hole into which a few of the corn seeds were dropped and then covered over lightly with ash. They found that the method of sowing in holes was much the more effective because the corn was given much better protection from birds. Moreover, it came up more evenly, and if sown in rows was much more easily kept free of weeds. The experiment also showed that it was possible to save half the amount of seed by placing it in holes.

They sowed an equal amount of corn by the same methods on the unburned area of woodland. Then they waited for the crops to grow. The resulting harvest justified the experiment although the yield of corn even in the burned area was much below the traditional return from the slash-and-burn methods which the experimenters quote: 'We know from Scania in Sweden that the harvest of rye in olden times was often 16-24 times the seed sown after burning, in comparison with 2-5 times in the normally tilled village fields.'

Although the trees were destroyed in the process of slash-and-burn, the stumps and the roots remained. If we can judge from what happened during the last century when the Americans and Canadians opened up new lands, no attempt was made at first to remove the stumps or the roots. The farmers cultivated round them. Early photographs of areas of North America show the cultivated fields with the stumps still standing. Presumably they were left until much later when they had rotted sufficiently to make grubbing or cutting them out less difficult.

It would be tempting to relate this ancient method of clearing and fertilizing the land to the modern practice of burning the stubble. Nearly every farmer in East Anglia now burns the straw on the harvest field, in the rows that have been delivered by the combine-harvester. But it is unlikely that stubble burning either cleanses the ground of weeds or adds very much to the soil's fertility. In the first place the stubble rarely burns evenly across the field; nor is the heat intense enough to destroy the seeds of tough and persistent weeds like wild oats. In proof of this many farmers point out that the weeds come up thicker and greener on those very rows where the fire has been. Again, the amount of ash left after stubble burning is negligible, and not to be compared with the rich wood-ash left after slash-and-burn. Perhaps the words of an East Anglian farmer, who still farms—as far as he can—according to the traditional methods, are sufficient comment:

'The trouble is that the present-day corn farmer doesn't know what to do with much of the straw left after harvest. Burning it solves the problem, and saves him the trouble of

Early Farmers: An Experiment

carting. But it wouldn't do to say this. He's got to find a respectable reason. This is it; and saying that burning the stubble does the land good is as neat a way as any of saving his face and soothing his own conscience.'

SOURCES AND BOOKS FOR FURTHER READING

The Agriculture History Review. Vol. V. Part 2, 1957
G. E. FUSSELL. *Farming Techniques from Prehistoric to Modern Times.* Pergamon Press, 1966
GORDON CHILDE. *What Happened in History.* Penguin Books, 1942
NORFOLK MUSEUMS. *4,000 Years of Norfolk Farming,* 1960

2

Preparing the Ground

The story of the Danish experiment has been told in some detail because it suggests that early man must have used fire extensively in clearing virgin land and in his efforts to grow crops. Scientists who have spent much time in Africa studying crops and soil have shown that fire played a great part in the agriculture of this continent. Examination of the soil (permanently altered by slash-and-burn farming) in densely forested areas has indicated very clearly that much of what was once considered virgin forest had previously supported a corn-growing people. As well as the characteristic soil left by former settlements they also found querns, primitive stone 'mills' for grinding corn, in apparently virgin areas. They have therefore suggested that the legend of 'darkest Africa' has given an entirely wrong idea of the age of the settlements and of the farming history of that continent.

All this implies that the landscape here in Britain—as in any long-settled country—is chiefly man-made. This is especially so in the arable-land areas where the fields, once cleared by methods such as the one described, have been laboriously extended, fenced and cultivated for hundreds of years; thereby not only yielding produce for man and animal but also preventing the legacy left by the early farmers from being lost by a reversion to the type of growth that is natural to a particular area.

The Danish account, which we can be pretty sure is relevant to farming in East Anglia, also shows the remarkable way in which certain farming practices have lasted from primitive times up to the recent past. Although it would be difficult to find instances of the slash-and-burn method of agriculture in Britain in recent years, we know that a similar method of paring and burning was successfully used in the seventeenth century by the great farming improver Sir Richard Weston. He enriched his land, as he said, 'by fire and water'—burning and irrigation; and his experiments were copied for many years after his death. He called the process of paring and burning *Devonshiring*, a name which shows not that the farmers of that county invented it but were great believers in its practice. Ash, too, is still used as a fertilizer as is soot; but up to the beginning of this century before artificial fertilizers were much used, turf was burned in kilns—so George Sturt wrote in his *Journals*—for the sole purpose of using the resulting ash as manure for the fields. This reminds us that where a farm or a field is called *Kiln*, not an uncommon name in East Anglia, the kiln which gives the field or the farm its name, may not have been used for firing draining tiles or pipes, or even bricks, but may well have been used for burning *flags* or turf for ash. Lime was sometimes burned in the same way.

This ancient experience of the fertilizing properties of ash was never forgotten. The Romans knew of it, and so did the medieval farmers in this country. Archaeologists are also aware of the use of ash on the land, for one of their methods of spotting an ancient settlement is by observing the darkness of the soil in its vicinity. Sometimes a place-name or the name of a field which contains the word *black* is a clue to the archaeologist, a reminder that the spot is worth looking at in case *black* refers to the ash-stained soil nearest an old settlement. There is, too, an old country proverb which emphasizes the truth that ash and domestic refuse and manure would be scattered on the land nearest the village itself. It says: 'The nearer the church the richer the land.' The church is the nucleus of most villages, and fields that were distant from the settlement grouped around it would naturally get only a marginal share of the village refuse.

The Danish experimenters discovered that by dropping the seeds of corn in holes made with a stick they were not only able to save corn but to harvest it more easily. This method of sowing is called *dibbing* or *dibbling*, and was much used in East Anglia up to the present century. But it did not oust the broadcast sowing of seed, a method that continued almost as

1. Dibbling

long. And this was in spite of the fact that Sir Hugh Plat, a clever Elizabethan farmer and innovator wrote in his book, *The Arte of Setting Corn* (1600), that by dibbling wheat he had increased its yield nearly four-fold. He wrote that the practice started through the accident of a 'silly wench' dropping seeds of wheat in holes intended for carrots. Dibbling was the forerunner of the present method of drilling corn by means of a seed-drill which deposits the seed evenly in one continuous hole or groove made by the drill coulter.

Early man prepared his land before sowing the corn by scratching it with a digging stick—a stick with its point hardened in the fire; or by a stick bent at one end and holding a stone hoe-blade such as is sometimes found on early farming sites. And from the hoe which was used or drawn by a man, or more probably by a woman, it was a natural progression to get an animal to draw the hoe through the soil, leaving the man to guide the stick and keep the blade in the soil. As a beast was now drawing the stick it could be made stouter and heavier, and so could the blade. And it would soon develop into a different implement—the simple plough, with its beam and its iron *share* (O.E. *scear*: *sceran*, to cut or shear) and its handle.

The earliest type of plough usually known as the *ard* (Lat. *aratrum*) scratched the surface of the soil rather than turned a true furrow. But this was sufficient where the soil was dry and friable, as it has been in southern Europe during the historical period. But to prepare heavy land that might become water-logged it was necessary to have a much heavier plough to turn the soil over, thus making a true furrow along which the excess water could run off. This heavy plough needed at least four oxen to draw it, as opposed to the lighter ard which needed a single beast or a pair at most. It was developed on the plains of northern Europe which experiences an amount of summer rainfall as well as the winter rainfall shared by the Mediterranean countries: and its use made it possible to prepare the ground for spring as well as winter corn—a big advantage over southern Europe whose dry summers made winter corn the usual crop and the ard the characteristic implement.

It is believed that the *Belgae*, a continental tribe of Celts who occupied roughly the area known as Belgium and came to Britain about 75 B.C., first brought a type of this heavy plough with them—just before Julius Caesar's first visit. But it is certain that this is the plough the Anglo-Saxons used to bring the rich clay-lands of southern and eastern England into cultivation, lands that the ard was not heavy enough to tackle. The Anglo-Saxon plough had a coulter or knife fixed vertically on the beam of the plough and just in front of the share. As the oxen drew the plough the coulter made the vertical cut in the land and the share the horizontal. It is unlikely that this plough, called a *carruca*, had a mouldboard. This is the curved plate behind the share which in a modern plough turns the slice of soil on to its back, making—so to speak—'the green sward black'. For there is no word for mouldboard in Old English. But we know from written evidence that the carruca turned a furrow; and it is probable there was a device, attached both to the share-beam and to the main plough-beam, which shouldered the furrow over as the plough went forward. There was a similar device—not a true mouldboard—in use in Kent until recent years.

The carruca, like the ard, was made almost entirely of wood: only the share, the coulter and the hake (the hook at the front of the plough to which the ox-harness was attached: O.E.: *haca*, a hook or pot-hook) were made of iron. An old wooden swing plough (a plough without wheels) was used in East Anglia within living memory, and this is in direct line with the early Saxon plough. Examples of it are to be found in provincial museums. It was used even up to the 'twenties, with two horses supplying the draught, to prepare the heavy clays of Norfolk and Suffolk for the corn for whose cultivation they are so suitable. This plough is another example of the continuity in British farming. Farming techniques and processes remained more-or-less the same for centuries because, until the recent past, farmers had to rely on basically the same means of power

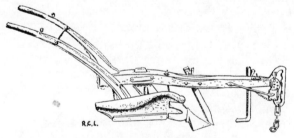

2. Cambridgeshire swing plough

as they had done since earliest times—man and animal power. It was not until the introduction of the machine on a large scale during the last sixty or seventy years that farming techniques were radically altered. Up to this time the old hand-tools, which were still used to a great extent on the farms of East Anglia, remained essentially the same in design as those used by the Romans.

Some of these old tools and their methods of use will be discussed in the following pages, but we should at this point touch on a process that was connected with preparing the seed-bed for the corn—another, incidentally, that lasted unchanged for at least 2,000 years. This is under-draining, some-

3.
Digging shoe (tied under boot)

times called thorough-draining, the technique by which a hollow drain is made under the soil into which excess water can soak and be taken off. The early farmers discovered through experience that land which remained damp or water-logged would not grow much corn. We know today that surface evaporation of moisture is accompanied by a loss of heat which considerably lowers the temperature of the seed-bed. Under-draining is therefore one of the farmer's most vital concerns in preparing his land for crops. The Romans knew the importance of this, and one of their writers, Palladius in his *De Re Rustica*, recommended filling shallow trenches with stones and then covering them up so that the water would drain away into a ditch cut at the side of the field.

A like practice lasted in East Anglia right up to this century, and there are many old farm-workers alive today who have constructed *bush-drains* whose design is similar to those used here in Romano-British times. But instead of packing the shallow trench with stones they rammed in hawthorn branches cut from the hedges, packing the clay back on top of the branches when they had done this. Even after the hawthorn had rotted the arch of clay still remained; and a good bush drain was in one way superior to an earthenware pipe-drain, so they maintain, because vermin were less likely to crawl along it and impede the flow of surplus water. But one of the reasons why this old method of draining was used in Suffolk even up to the 'thirties was undoubtedly its cheapness. During the agricultural depression of the inter-war period many farmers could not afford to buy draining pipes, and bush-draining was preferred because it was cheaper and was a traditional skill that had survived and still served the purpose.

To make a bush-drain the ploughman first ploughed a furrow. This was then cleaned out and deepened by a spade with a rather long tapering blade. After the trench had been cleaned out to a *spit*'s depth—the depth of the blade—another

4.
Bush-draining tool or
cley

tool was used to make a smaller channel at the bottom to take the actual bushes. This is a special bush-draining tool: many of these tools are still to be found in barns and tool sheds; many of them have been converted to a dozen other uses on the farm or in the garden now that bush-draining is no longer practised.

But under-draining with earthenware pipes is still one of the most important jobs in connection with the seed-bed, but like most farm-processes in East Anglia today it has been highly mechanized; and it is very expensive. Yet as one farmer recently told me: 'Even if you spend £2,000 in under-draining a field you'll get it back in two or three years by the increased yield of corn following the draining.' Farmers know, too, that under-draining is not only profitable on heavy land: it is just as worthwhile on the lighter soils. For as Henry Stephens, a nineteenth-century writer on farming, pointed out: 'Land which retains water in winter is in a bad state, though it should be burnt up in summer; and burning requires draining to cure it. Lands burn when naturally light and thin, when they rest on a retentive subsoil. Being thin, they are quickly saturated with rain in winter; and being light, the water in them is soon evaporated in summer; and should drought follow, the crop on them is burnt up. Now draining is the best preventive against the evil of burning, since drains serve as reservoirs for moisture to be taken up to the plants by capillary attraction through the dry subsoil in summer, and thereby counteract the effects of drought; and they act as ducts for the conveyance of superfluous water in winter, and thereby coun-teract the effects of cold and wet. I have cured burning land by draining. Draining thus acts in a double and opposite manner, supplying moisture in summer and keeping the land dry in winter. What greater benefits can be expected from any opera-tion affecting the land?'

The above helps to explain why the Romans developed under-draining so early. For the conditions as described here by Stephens—wet winters and dry summers—exactly fit the Mediterranean type of climate; and burnt-up (or *scalled* land as they call it in Suffolk), must have been a problem that Mediterranean farming had to face at a very early stage of its evolution.

SOURCES AND BOOKS FOR FURTHER READING

LORD ERNLE. *English Farming Past and Present*. Sixth Edition, Heinemann, 1961
G. E. FUSSELL. *Farming Techniques from Prehistoric to Modern Times*
HENRY STEPHENS. *The Book of the Farm*. Blackwood, 1877
NORMAN E. LEE. *Harvests and Harvesting*. Cambridge, 1960
C. S. ORWIN. *The History of English Farming*. Nelson, 1949
GEORGE STURT. *Journals*, Vol. 2 (p. 496), Cambridge University Press, 1967

3

Sowing the Seed and Harrowing

After living at Blaxhall, a small Suffolk village, for some years after the last war I realized that we were witnessing the end of the old farming. One fact made this apparent: during the eight years I lived there nearly all the farm horses disappeared from the land, and their places were taken by the tractor. But many of the oldest generation in the village—men and women who were born around 1880—grew up under the old hand-tool farming; and the life they knew and described to me was the kind of life that had been linked with this farming for centuries. The men had all harvested corn using the scythe; some of them had even used the sickle; and they had in their keeping the traditional farming lore, the old working knowledge that had been handed down for generations.

Although John Fowler of Leeds had perfected a method of ploughing with a steam engine and ploughing tackle as early as 1858, the steam plough did not cause a big change in farming. Its impact was felt only here and there, on land and under conditions where it was suitable for it to operate. The first big change in the tools of farming in the corn areas was the introduction of the self-binder harvester which cut the corn and tied it into sheaves ready for shocking. This reaper-binder was marketed from the early 1880's onwards but the first self-binder did not reach Blaxhall, for instance, until the first years of this century. And even though methods soon began to change on the farms after this, it was not until the First World War that the old system of farming and the way of life linked with it began finally to break up. The internal combustion engine, fed by oil or petrol, soon proved itself more suitable for farming needs than the steam engine; and in the space of a generation or so it quickly did away with farming processes and customs that had persisted for thousands of years.

Yet the tools of the old farming still remained, and not all of them were left to rust. For although they had been out-dated by the coming of the machine to the farm they were still used on the allotments or *yards* attached to the cottages. Indeed the farm workmen at Blaxhall continued to use the old tools for a generation after they had been displaced on the farms. At that time it was clear to someone like myself, coming into the village from outside, that the men and the tools they used were historical documents that could give accurate information about farming methods, such as sowing corn broadcast, harvesting with the serrated sickle, threshing with the flail, all of which had lasted since Biblical times. In fact one could imagine that when this old generation of country people read of these identical methods in the Bible or heard them expounded in school, church or chapel, they would believe their own way of life—of sowing, tending and harvesting in essentially the same way as of old—was part of the eternal pattern of things and would go on for ever. Therefore change and the machine when they did come were slow of acceptance; and we can excuse the older country people for their reaction, especially when we remember that changes were often brought in during farming depressions when jobs were few and threatened to be even fewer by the coming of the labour-saving machines.

A sower went forth to sow—the Biblical image of broadcast sowing became a symbol of the old farming; and the broad-casting of seed lasted long after the development of dibbling and the perfecting of the corn-drill by Jethro Tull, the eighteenth-century Berkshire farmer. Some East Anglian farmers used the broadcast method to sow the headlands—that is the outside strip of land close to the hedges—of a field that had been sown with the drill. But broadcast sowing was used regularly up to 1914 in East Anglia for the sowing of small seeds like clover or turnips. Like most of the old farming methods, broadcast sowing looks deceptively simple. But it is a very skilled job, and it needed long experience and concentration to sow a field of corn so that there were no *missed bits*, pieces where no seed had fallen and which therefore showed up bare when the corn sprouted.

A Blaxhall farmer, Robert H. Sherwood (1885–1963), told me how many of the old farming skills went out during his working life. One of these related to the broadcast sowing of seed. Broadcast sowing with one hand was not easy: sowing with two hands was extremely difficult: 'We grew a lot of English white clover. Practically every farmer round here used to grow it at one time. And now, well, I don't know anyone who grows it at all. Sowing it was really a very skilful job indeed. You were lucky in those days if you had a man on the farm who could do it. You sowed only about two pounds, or half a peck at the outside, of seed per acre; and this had to be sown in step with two hands alternately. The sower took only a pinch of seed between his thumb and finger at a time, and it was broadcast as he walked in step [synchronizing foot with hand]. He used a seed-container, which was called a hod, hung on his chest with a strap over his neck; and he dipped his hands into this alternately and just took a pinch out and it was sown. And if when the crop came up, he'd missed a foot in the whole field—well, he would never hear the last of it!'

Dibbling, as already mentioned, was practised alongside broadcast sowing. But it was not until the end of the eighteenth century, during the farming revolution of that period, that it was used and experimented with systematically. Arthur Young, the first Secretary of the Board of Agriculture, described how dibbling was carried out in Suffolk: 'A man with a dibbler in each hand walked backwards on the *flag* (the furrow slice) and made holes in the seed-bed. A child or woman followed him

C   33

with a hod of corn seed, dropping a few seeds into each hole.'
Young also recorded that in Suffolk: 'Beans have been dibbled
in a row on every flag, by others on every other flag. Dibbling
is the best and most effective method of cultivating beans.'
The farmers at this time were also experimenting with dibbling,
comparing it with the corn-drill which was just beginning to
come into general use. A Suffolk farmer, Arthur Biddell of
Playford, dibbled and drilled different strains of wheat on equal
areas of land in order to compare the yield. Here is an entry
from his Day Book or farming diary:
'*Wheat Sowing*, 1821:
'Finished in Home Barn feild Nov. 23rd. The 1st Dibbled
Stetch nearest the Gate is of Wheat from Mr Fuller's. The next
(2nd) Dibbled Stetch of Wheat is from Scotch Wheat or North
Country from Ely's; the third Dibbled Stetch is of North
Country Wheat (such as a coomb is left). The 4th Dibbled
Stetch is wheat of my own growth. All the rest of the feild is
Drilled. The further side with Wheat from the North—such as
on the 2nd Dibbled Stetch. About 2 Acres on this side is
Drilled with such as 3rd Dibbled Stetch. The Headlands all
round the feild is rather mixed.'

(Two East Anglian terms in this entry may need explanation.
A stetch is the unit of ploughed land between two furrows.
Its width varied according to the type of land—wide on light

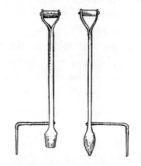

5. Dibbles with spacing bars

land, narrow on heavy. It is known by various names: ridge, rigg, land, rap, stitch; and it is similar to the *selion* or strip of the open-fields. A coomb or comb is a unit of measure, equalling four bushels, or half a quarter.)

In Helmingham, the village where I now live, the old dibbling skill has been handed down directly from this time; and there is a reason why it has been used without a break. Following the Napoleonic Wars and the enclosure of the open fields and commons, which had been proceeding with great pace since 1760, there was terrible distress among the agricultural workers. Many of them, after they had been forced to give up their small pieces of land and their rights of common, had lost heart: they felt that as day-labourers, often only partially employed, they had no real vital interest in the land as they had before; and this was even harder to bear than the poverty which was the more apparent mark of their new condition. Arthur Young, although he was one of the foremost advocates of enclosures, showed very clearly what enclosures meant in human terms: 'Go,' he said, 'to an alehouse kitchen of an old enclosed country, and there you will see the origin of poverty and the poor-rates. For whom are they to be sober? For whom are they to save? (such are their questions). For the parish? If I am diligent, shall I have leave to build a cottage? If I am sober, shall I have land for a cow? If I am frugal, shall I have half an acre of potatoes? You offer no motives; you have nothing but a parish officer and a workhouse. Bring me another pot!'

The poverty of the displaced farm-workers and the general poverty in the countryside, caused by the farming depressions during the first half of last century, aroused national concern; and the Government attempted to meet the distress by allocating allotments, small pieces of land, to workers so that they could add to their meagre wage by growing some of their own produce, and—almost as important—so that they could win back some of their self-respect. Enlightened landowners, careful of the welfare of the people on their own estate began to re-plan their holdings. They sank capital in building model cottages, each surrounded by a piece of land which the tenant could cultivate more or less in his own way.

John Tollemache, whose family had lived at Helmingham Hall for centuries, laid out his estate in this way at the middle of the century. It covered many parishes, and he built estate cottages here and there in each village, each pair of cottages with a piece of land surrounding or adjoining it. The village of Helmingham remains almost exactly as John Tollemache planned it; and the school which he built in 1853 at a cost of £1,200 is still open. Each pair of semi-detached cottages— *double-dwellers* they call them here—is built on an acre of ground, so that each tenant had nearly a half-acre of land to farm. I write *had* because, after operating for over a century, modern changes have made John Tollemache's system unworkable. In many of the estate cottages today only older farm-workers are living, men who have seen the present revolution of farming right from the beginning. Many of them are of an advanced age, and there are few younger farm-workers to replace them. They are therefore unable to farm their half-acres as they used to. Nor is there need. Thus only last year (1966) many of the half-acre pieces were taken back into the farmland from which they were first carved out.

But an occasional retired worker still cultivates his piece in the old way, men like Joe Thompson (born 1901) and A. W. Lankester (born 1893); and Caleb Howe (1886–1967) dug his half-acre until a year or so before his death. They used the old hand-tools—flail, scythe, sickle, bagging hook, dibble and small seed-drill—for over half a century after these implements had been displaced from the farm by machines. This is illustrated by Joe Thompson's account of dibbling:

'I learnt the proper way to dibble from a very old man, Charlie Sharman. I was quite young at the time. Old Charlie must have first used the dibbles in the field round about a hundred years ago. One of the last times he used them—I recollect him telling me—was to dibble winter beans. All of us round here used to grow about a quarter of an acre of corn on our allotments; and I used to dibble my corn as most of the others did. Just after the First World War when times were very bad I used to go round dibbling corn and so on in other people's allotments just to earn a shilling or two.

'I've got my two dibbles here, as you see. But I rarely use the two of them together now. I use one regularly as a sort of general purpose tool on the allotment. But when I was going round dibbling, I used to put a line down to start with just to guide me. When you were dibbling in the field you didn't need anything to guide you: you just followed the flag, that's the furrow. But where the land was flat you had no guide so I put down the string. Then I used to dibble round and round this line making two rows each time. I went round just like a horseman did when he was a-ploughing a stetch, walking backwards and putting my feet down exactly as the old Ashbocking man had taught me. I used to get someone from the house to drop the seed into the holes I made with the dibble. I then used to cover up by raking the land over. On the farm, of course, they used the harrow after a stetch had been dibbled.'

Before hearing Joe Thompson's account a few entries in Helmingham School log-book had set me a puzzle. They read: *Wednesday, 21st October, 1863.* Several children absent from Lower School, dropping wheat.

16th March, 1875. Several absent from Upper Classes. Seed time. Children wanted for dropping.

It was clear that here were instances of children helping with sowing winter and spring corn—dropping the seeds into the holes made by the dibbles. But why should farmers be using the dibble in an advanced farming area 130–140 years after Tull had invented his seed-drill? The question answered itself after I had spoken to Joe Thompson, Dan Pilgrim, Lester Brett, Caleb Howe and other Helmingham smallholders. By and large, it was not on the farms that the dibbles were used but on the allotments; and many allotment holders kept their children at home during the spring and autumn sowing, to drop seeds;

and the teachers could do little about it. Yet the Helmingham schoolmaster, Henry Orchard, wrote on February 20th, 1874:

'Large numbers have been absent working on the fields "dropping" beans and peas. Thin attendance in consequence.'

This proves that the farmers also employed children when they dibbled beans and peas. But for beans, at least, some farmers were already using the bean drill. This was a kind of hod attached to the plough. The beans dropped into the furrow as it was turned over; and they were covered up by another plough following behind and turning another furrow.

It was in such areas as Helmingham, where dibbles have been used without interruption right up to the present that some of the lore connected with them has survived. Here are two rhymes which the children recited occasionally while dibbling to break up the monotony of the work:

> *Four seeds in a hole:*
> *One for the rook, and one for the crow;*
> *And one to rot, and one to grow.*

or: *Four seeds in a hole:*
> *One for the buds (birds),*
> *One for the meece (mice),*
> *And two for Maaster.*

The more generous allowance for the master, hoped for in the second rhyme, must have been realized on many sowings where corn was being dibbled. Mice, it appears, were very rarely enemies to corn. One farm-worker, Sam Friend (born 1888) told me: 'I don't know that the meece would get at the corn much. If you have any peas, though, you had to look out for meece then. But I've seen rats burrow under the flag to get at the beans that had been sown in behind the plough that had an old bean drill fixed to it.'

Alongside the dibbles the broadcast machine or seed-barrow was used; and there are still a few left on the farms in the corn areas. The seed-barrow was first made in the early nineteenth century, and is of simple design: a long rectangular hod containing the seed lies across a barrow. A spindle inside the hod is joined to the axle of the barrow wheel by an endless cord. As the sower pushed the barrow the spindle in the hod revolved, and attachments to this ejected the seed which fell in a rough lane between six and eight feet wide, depending on the length of the hod. Latterly many farmers in Suffolk used the seed-barrow for sowing clover seed which was afterwards harrowed.

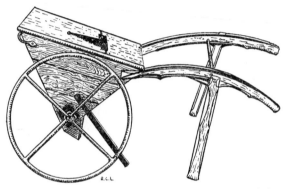

6. Bean-barrow or -drill. A similar hod was fixed behind the plough

Dibbles have not been much used for drilling corn in the Helmingham allotments in recent years because Joe Thompson bought a small two-coulter seed drill, made on the same principle as the famous Smyth drill with a lever coulter. It was made in Helmingham or an adjoining village; and Joe Thompson bought it forty-five years ago from a man who had himself used it for as long before this. It has been difficult to unearth the drill's early history, but it was undoubtedly made for the Helmingham half-acres. It was probably constructed by the local blacksmith with the help of the wheelwright. It is still being used, as corn and beans are occasionally grown here in the allotments to provide fodder for animals. For many years Joe Thompson has hired it out to his neighbours at a shilling a time. He recalls that he and three neighbours 'on a short Saturday afternoon' drilled an acre of wheat at Helmingham allotments: 'There were two pulling: one in the shafts of the drill, another hitched up like a trace-hoss, the third walking behind the drill to see it was running right, and the fourth raking over.'

Drilling in the field was much different. Here is an account of drilling given by George Sadler (1905–1966) a Whittlesford, Cambridgeshire farmer. He was referring to his father's farm, about forty years ago: 'When I first started drilling I was more or less a drill-boy because I was only seventeen. I had to go and lead the two front horses on. We used to have one in the shafts in those days. I don't think it was a Smyth drill but I know one day we were drilling some winter barley. It was a November morn, and I'd been leading these horses; and it was close and the sweat was running off them. Well, my father came down and he said to the drill-man:

' "Where's that boy, George?"

'The drill man said: "Look between those hosses!"

'There was so much steam coming away from them horses he couldn't see anything of me.

'We used to have to drill ten acres a day. And you had to drill it—to the inch! No one must be able to find fault with it; and when it was done you couldn't see a quarter of an inch out. It had to be done right. They took some pride in their work in those days. They were really interested in it; and the old horsemen would go to the pubs on a Saturday night, and they'd call out to someone:

' "I bet my bit o' drawin' [ploughing] is better'n yours," or if you were a young lad just started ploughing they'd say:

' "Well, you made a darn good job of it for the first time. But you got one or two hand-shakes in it. But never mind, you'll be a better man the next time."

'If we'd got a 25-acre field to do—we had one or two of those—my father, he'd slip us in there on a Thursday. Ten acres a day and five acres on a Saturday. (When I first started there weren't no half-day. We finished work at 6 o'clock on a Saturday night. But as times got better they left off at 2 o'clock, then at 1 o'clock. But the horseman still had to do his hosses; and he would do 'em! he wouldn't shun 'em. He go back after dinner to finish 'em.) But we went into this 25-acre field, and we weren't looking for a job, I can tell you, to drill 25 acres in two and a half days. It was six o'clock in the morning and unyoke at 2 o'clock. Perhaps we'd go and get a load of straw after dinner. They'd be threshing somewhere on the farm and you'd get a load of straw to put in the horse-yard. As they were threshing they'd get the stack three parts of the way up, then

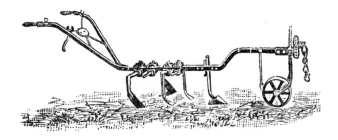

7. Cottis plough (with duck-foot tines) for hoeing between cattle-beet or winter beans

they'd push this straw down on top of you. Us boys—well, we'd be tired by then—but these older men would push a load down on you at a time, smother you, cover you up, and cover the darned hosses up as well.

'Well, after you'd got your drilling done you got your seeds to drill in. That was another tricky job—drilling the undersown seeds into the barley. When you turned the drill round you didn't allow it skid round or else you'd be cutting into your barley. You'd got to run that round almost on a *pivol*. But you'd got to get that wheel straight up again. My word, I know that many's the time I've patted a place down with my hands if I'd made a bit of a mess-up there, in case anybody should see it.

'When the barley was up we'd put in clovers or sanfoins or a number of different kinds of seed. There used to be a bigger variety grown in those days. There'd be kidney-vetch, linseed— all sorts of seed we used to grow. Then we had to rib-roll that. Three hosses on a rib-roll. I remember one day I was rib-rolling. We had three hosses on this roll, and every little bit of furrow they went over they jumped up in the air. My father came down and he said to me:

' "After dinner I'm going to send someone down to put those shafts on the outside."

'The shafts were in the middle, you see, and horse on the trace on each side of the horse in the shafts. He said:

' "You'll have two horses on that roll tomorrow." He knew by the look of me I didn't approve of it, and he added: "Otherwise, they're going to run away with you and smash up the damn lot. They don't get enough work. You keep feeding 'em and feeding 'em up!" He didn't know we'd been pinching corn specially to feed these horses.'

Drilling the corn was a very important job, as it still is, and the farmer himself was never very far off while it was being done. Yet a great deal of the arable farmer's skill goes into the preparation of the seed-bed and into choosing the exact time to sow his seed. Many of the old farmers before the farms were mechanized sowed only when the moon was waxing, and some even do so today. But all farmers were very particular about the seed-bed and were very careful to make it fine as they could. They would not start sowing until the soil was in good heart, with a good tilth and enough heat in it to prevent the seed from lying cold for too long before germinating. One farmer of the old school boasted to me that he could tell the state of his land and whether he could sow simply by crumbling some of the soil in his hand and then walking over the land. He claimed he could feel the state of the soil through his boots. That he was acting in a traditional way is shown by a quotation from a sixteenth-century writer, John Fitzherbert, who wrote in his *Book of Husbandry*:

Sowing the Seed and Harrowing

'Go uppon the lande that is plowed, and if it synge or crye or make any noyse under thy fete, then it is to wete to sowe. And if it make no noyse and wyll beare thy horses, thanne sowe in the name of God.'

An old farm foreman, Arthur Chaplin of Stowupland, said very much the same when he was describing how one of the men who farmed the land before the coming of the tractors, sized up a new farm when he was taking it over:

'He wouldn't plant much at first. He'd wait a bit and see what the land was like: he'd prove the land first. A good practical man would hold on for a few weeks and get the feel of the land under his feet. He'd walk on it and feel it through his boots, and see if it was in good heart, before he planted anything. He'd sow only when he knew what the land was fit for.'

Then when he sowed spring corn he tested whether the seed-bed was warm enough by drawing the back of his hand across the soil. In this part of East Anglia some of the old school went much farther than this. To make doubly sure that the land was warm enough to sow barley, they took down their trousers and sat bare on the seed-bed. This was not an uncommon practice in the Mendlesham and Stowupland areas of Suffolk during the last century. And it appears that, if after this fundamental exercise the land was deemed fit for sowing, the barley would germinate quickly and be up in three days.

In harrowing the ground, too, the feel of the land was as important as its appearance to the farmer who tilled his land with horses. When the seed was dibbled or sown broadcast, the harrow was used after the sowing. But in sowing with the drill—as is universal on the farms of Britain today—the land is harrowed with heavy gang harrows before sowing to give the soil a proper tilth: after sowing it is harrowed with a light harrow. A good farmer can recognize a well-harrowed piece of land not only by its sight but by its feel: for efficient harrowing makes the ground feel uniformly consistent to the tread of the foot. The breaking up of the small clods of earth—the comminuting of the soil, as it is called—to give it a good uniform

43

texture or tilth is important because it will help to keep the seed-bed at a more equable temperature, not admitting the rain into it too quickly or letting out much moisure when the weather is very dry.

George Sadler has also given us a picture of harrowing behind the drill:

'After leading the horses on the drill I sometimes went harrowing behind. We always had to keep one bout behind the drill in case the *counter* [drill-coulter] got blocked, and the drill

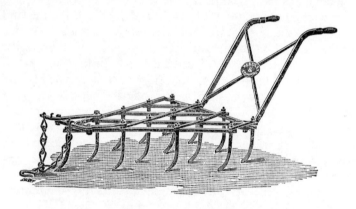

8. Crab harrow

man wanted to drill that piece again. After the horseman had knocked off with his drill—after he'd done his ten acres, perhaps a little more to get a little forward by Saturday—we had to do this extra bout of harrowing. We were always behind, and even when we finished that we'd have to take back the cart we'd brought the corn in. It was often about 2.30 before we got back to dinner.

'We used to start putting the collars on the horses at six o'clock in the morning. Then we got down to the field. We reckon we'd do the headlands and about two bouts up the field by 8 o'clock; and then we'd have our breakfast. Then the harrow-boy would have a hook-stick he used to lift the harrows up with. As he stopped at each headland to clean his harrows he'd put his hook-stick in the hedge and pull a bit of rotten wood out. Or if we were coming up the road past a straw-stack—there were plenty of those at that time of day—we'd get a nice bundle of straw and put it on the horses' hames, and take it up the field. If we were lucky and were near where there were sheep we used to have a hurdle as well. And we'd break up this hurdle, a nice ash one; then we'd have a lovely fire for breakfast.

'Some of the old men used to have a herring, get a stick out of the hedge and make a fork out of it and toast the herring. Some of those that were fairly well off in those days they'd have a can of tea with a cork tied on to the handle so when it got hot it didn't blow off. I never had a can—never enough money to buy one—I had a bottle; and I used to put the bottle by the fire and often as not it broke, and I didn't have a drink all day unless I went and got some water out of the sheep's trough. After we'd had our breakfast, if we'd burnt a hurdle the old man who'd sat with his fork toasting the herring used to pick out all the nails out of the fire. Then we'd plough them in so if anyone came round they couldn't see we'd burnt a hurdle. If they did we'd get the sack.'

The form of harrow undoubtedly used by early man was the bush-harrow; and it was one of those implements that was used until the recent past. Arthur Chaplin described how he used to treat his meadows in the spring:

'Earlier in the year you spreed [spread] all the mole-hills with a spade. If you left the mole-hills untouched until the harrowing and rolling you'd be doing harm because the harrow would just skim them off and then you'd have a pan-cake of pressed mud, caked hard; and no grass would get through that easily. We did the meadows with an old bush-harrow.'

I can speak for myself concerning the making and using of a bush-harrow on a meadow. This was in Glamorgan in the early 'twenties. Making a bush-harrow was a simple operation: it was our practice to cut down a few hawthorn bushes having good, strong boles. We then laid them down evenly and placed a heavy log over them. After tying the boles to the log we hitched it to a horse, getting him to drag the log and bushes up and down the meadow, making as even and regular lines as we could. I must confess that my standards in harrowing a meadow were not as high as the Suffolk farm-worker's when he treated a field of young wheat. Arthur Chaplin told me:

'It was a sight to see the wheat or the meadow just after it had been harrowed—especially when the sun was on it. If there was a tree in the middle of the pasture I was harrowing, I did my best to keep the harrow *square*, to go right round the tree and carry on the other side in exactly the same line. So if somebody were to look at this field as they were passing, they'd think and wonder, because it would look as though the harrow had gone plumb through the tree without stopping.'

But at least I can confirm the beauty of a well-harrowed spring meadow: the alternate lanes of contrasting green, one glinting in the clear light, the next lane appearing as a darker, more subdued under-growth waiting its time to burgeon. The field then has a formal splendour that is in arresting contrast to the spring explosion of the trees and the enclosing hedgerows.

SOURCES AND BOOKS FOR FURTHER READING

Helmingham (Suffolk) School Log Book, 1863–1902

M. K. ASHBY. *Joseph Ashby of Tysoe*. Cambridge University Press, 1961

W. E. TATE. *The English Village Community*, Gollancz, 1967

The Horse in the Furrow. Faber and Faber, 1960 (Paperbound edition, 1967)

4

Weeding

The philosopher may say that a weed is simply a plant growing in the wrong place; but the farmer and the gardener have to be single-minded about it. To the farmer, at least, weeds are *rubbish*; and they must come out or else his crops will suffer. The early farmers solved the problem of a decreasing yield in a very simple way: they left the land which had become exhausted, or where weeds had got the better of the crop, and they moved on to another area that had been cleared and burned ready for sowing. But when land became less plentiful the farmer and gardener discovered that they could deal with weeds by digging them in before they seeded: in this way the rotting plants helped to manure the seed-bed. For those weeds like couch or spear-grass, whose roots do not rot easily, the only method was—and still is—to keep on worrying them; ploughing, cultivating, scarifying the land, 'keep on a-turning of it over' as an East Anglian countryman put it, until the roots come to the surface, are dried out and killed.

The Romans knew this and practised rotating their crops and fallowing, as the poet Virgil wrote in the first book of *The Georgics*, a practical manual for farmers. Roman farmers left fields untilled as much to keep down the weeds as to allow the land to recover. 'Plough', Virgil advised; 'let your strong bulls turn over the rich soil in the early months of the year . . . lest, later on, weeds stand in the way and take the smile off the face of your crops.'

47

Weeding

The Anglo-Saxon and later the medieval farmers fallowed or rested a third of their arable land every year. In one huge open-field they planted winter corn—usually in October or early November—and then in the second field spring corn was sown in March. The third field remained bare. Cattle and sheep fed on the weeds and grasses that grew on this fallow land. But the farmer was careful not to let the weeds go to seed. He therefore ploughed his land at least three times while it was lying fallow. We know this from old farming documents; and the practice is very simply written down by Thomas Tusser, the sixteenth-century writer who followed the tradition of Hesiod and Virgil and wrote his farming maxims in verse. His chief work was *Five Hundred Good Points of Husbandry*; and he gave his advice in four-line stanzas of simple verse in order that the farmers could easily memorize it. The first ploughing or fallow should be done as early as possible—in April if the weather allows it; the second should come in May, at the latest, and should be a shallow ploughing—just deep enough to destroy the weeds.

But as Tusser wrote in *April's Husbandry* the time of the ploughings varied from county to county:

> *In Cambridgeshire forward to Lincolnshire way,*
> *the champion maketh his fallow in May;*
> *Then thinking so doing one tillage worth twain,*
> *By forcing of weed by that means to refrain.*

> *If April be dripping, then do I not hate*
> *(for him that hath little) his fallowing late;*
> *Else otherwise fallowing timely is best,*
> *for saving of cattle, of plough, and the rest.*

The champion does not refer to the medieval farmer's abilities; nor is it Tusser's irony. It indicates simply the land he farmed —the open-field, the *champagn* (Lat. *campania*). Enclosure of the open-fields started very early in East Anglia which was Tusser's own region. He called the land that had been enclosed

48

1. A SMYTH STEERAGE CORN-DRILL. Blaxhall Hall, Suffolk

2. BRANDESTON (SUFFOLK) FORGE (*c.* 1880)

3. BRANDESTON STREET (*c.* 1910)

4. AN EARLY FORD TRACTOR (Brandeston *c.* 1917) Model T Ford in background. A ploughman with a pair of horses first *drew* or set out this field. He also *shut-up* or finished off with a horse-plough

severall. It was farmed in *severalty*, that is, in separate units under individual ownership as opposed to the communal ownership of the open-fields. Here in fact in Tusser's day we find the beginnings of the movement to enclose land: it was a time when the medieval economy of farming for use, or subsistence, was giving way to the modern development of farming chiefly for the market. This movement continued through the following centuries reaching its peak from about 1760–1845.

It is perhaps worth noting that the word *severals* survives in East Anglia as a relic of these early enclosures. Three *severals* come to mind immediately, denoting the name of a disputed piece of parish land, an area in a town, and the site of a hospital—in Suffolk, Cambridgeshire and Essex respectively.

May was the month, however, for the second ploughing in Norfolk and Suffolk:

> *In May at the furthest twifallow thy land,*
> *much drought may else after cause plough for to stand.*

The third ploughing in July was meant to finish off the weeds completely; but if the season allowed it, another extra ploughing later on would not come amiss.

> *Thry fallow betime for destroying of weed,*
> *lest thistle and dock fall a-blooming and seed:*
> *Such season may chance it shall stand thee upon*
> *to till it again ere summer be gone.*

But May was the month for the great attack on the weeds that were in the crops:

> *In May get a weed-hook, a crotch and a glove,*
> *and weed out such weeds as the corn do not love.*
> *For weeding of winter corn now it is best;*
> *but June is the better for weeding the rest.*

And later in the month he enjoined:

> *Then after a shower to weeding a snatch,*
> *more easily weed with the root to dispatch.*

D   49

This last instruction is explained by an entry in the fourteenth-century records of a Suffolk manor. On this manor sixty *sarclers* or weeders worked on the fields during a period. When the weather was dry they used weed-hooks and forked sticks or crotches as recommended by Tusser: in wet weather they used a weeding-tongs or nippers to pluck out the weeds by the roots from the soft soil.

A thirteenth-century author, Walter of Henley, wrote that thistles should not be cut before St John's Day (June 24th), and this advice was later enshrined in verse:

> *Thistles cut in May*
> *Come again next day.*
> *Thistles cut in June*
> *Come up again soon.*
> *Cut them in July,*
> *They'll be sure to die.*

The weed-hook or little sickle is pictured in use in the fourteenth-century *Luttrell Psalter*. Cutting out weeds with a hook is another of the old farming practices that persisted right up to the present day. There are many old women alive in Suffolk who cut thistles out of the corn, using weed-hooks exactly as did their medieval forebears. William Cobbold (1883–1964), a

9.
Weed-hook

bailiff on a Suffolk farm, told me that in the early 'twenties he employed a gang of women to go into a field with weed-hooks and cut the thistles out of the corn. But some people still use the hook though not for weeding corn. Like many of the old farming tools the weed-hook has developed a secondary use, and women going blackberry-picking find it a very useful stick to take with them.

The dock was another persistent weed which called for a special tool to deal with it. This was the dock-spud or chisel— a sharp, rectangular blade a couple of inches wide, fitted at the end of a stick. The worker stabbed the blade down into the root of the dock as far as he could. The old type of farmer often had a dock-spud fitted to his walking-stick, and even the most leisurely walk round his fields could be turned to some profit by an occasional prod at a weed that had boldly reared its head to threaten the crops.

A reading of Tusser reveals another instance of how long these old farming practices lasted: he mentioned the use of a glove while weeding; this was to protect the hands of the weeder when he carried the weeds he had cut out of the corn. But even after the most thorough weeding many still remained in the corn until it was harvested. It was necessary then for the reapers, using sickles and handling each bunch of corn as they cut it, to wear gloves to protect their hands from the thistles: indeed, Tusser advised giving the reapers gloves. And Sir John Cullum of Hawstead in Suffolk, writing in 1784, mentioned that the medieval practice of presenting gloves to the reapers still went on in his village: 'The agreement between the farmers and the hired harvesters is made on Whitsun Monday. Harvest gloves of 7d a pair are still presented.' But the custom continued well into this century. Arthur Chaplin recalled that nearly sixty years ago *glove-money* was one of the items on the harvest contract or agreement between the farmer and his workers to take in the corn on a Stowupland farm. Each worker got 2s 6d for gloves to protect his hands during the harvest.

Weeding

But the control of weeds was closely bound up with the method of sowing the seed. As Jethro Tull saw, if you drilled your seed in rows you could weed the corn as it was growing; and in theory, at least, keep the whole crop entirely free. Tull believed that hoeing between the rows of corn would give the farmer a tremendous advantage in his battle with the weeds; and his book, *Horse-Hoeing Husbandry* (1733) was one of the main stimuli to the farming revolution of the nineteenth century, proving Tull to be yet another genius who got little recognition in his own life-time. But corn was also hoed by hand, probably when it had been dibbled, for many years after broadcast sowing had largely been displaced, as an old lady in Blaxhall recalled. She was born in the 'eighties; and she remembers her mother telling her that on the day in March when she was born the Blaxhall women were out hoeing wheat on one of the farms.

Under the old farming of pre-machine days a good test of a man's farming skill was to observe whether his land was clean or foul with weeds. If he got on top of his weeds and successfully kept them under one could be sure he was a good farmer. This skill is well summarized in the saying: *Farm in front of your rubbish*; and a Blaxhall farmer, W. A. Peake, explained to me what was behind it:

'A good farmer sowed his seed so he could take his crop of corn before the rubbish came on. You had to be a good farmer to do that, a good practical farmer. And you wouldn't get the knowledge out of a book. There was no short cut: farming was an art and few men had it unless they'd come by it the hard way. Out of the gentlemen who came into farming at that time [before mechanization] only about one in twenty could make it go: the others had to have a skilled man to manage the farm for 'em. But the skill has gone out of farming now. Today, if a man takes over a farm and gets into a muddle, he has the fertilizers, the sprays and the weedkillers—the whole lot to get him out of it.'

But, whatever our opinion about this, it is true that weeding demonstrates as effectively as any mechanized process on the present day farm how extensive has been the farming revolution in this century. The ancient conflict between man and weeds goes on still, but its focus has completely shifted. It is not so much under the captaincy of the farmer who at one time constantly walked his fields, watching his crops, sending his forces here with hooks and tongs, and anticipating an outbreak there by deploying his ploughs and his scarifiers. The main battle is now joined in the laboratories. The scientists are now the captains, and the farmer is their trusting—some say too trusting—lieutenant. And to a modern farmer in Britain Tusser's ancient mandate: *Go muster thy servants: be captain thyself*, must sound rather out of date. For the farmer is now one of a much larger army than he used to be, and yet in a mustering of his servants he does not find many to stand immediately behind him.

SOURCES AND BOOKS FOR FURTHER READING

VIRGIL. *The Georgics.* Translated by C. Day Lewis, Cape, 1946
SIR JOHN CULLUM. *The History of Hawsted* (Hawstead, Suffolk), Second Edition, J. Nichols, 1813
LORD ERNLE. *English Farming Past and Present*
H. A. BEECHAM AND J. W. Y. HIGGS. *The Story of Farm Tools.* Evans Brothers, 1961
Ask the Fellows Who Cut the Hay. Faber and Faber, 1962 (Second Edition) Paperbound Edition, 1965
C. S. ORWIN. *The History of English Farming*

5

The Growing Corn

The corn farmer has many jobs to do between the sowing of his seed and the harvesting of the crop. Today he does most of these with the machines: he sprays his crops or hoes between the rows of beet and beans with a tractor; he keeps the birds away by cartridges timed to explode at intervals or by curious, multi-coloured scarecrows. With the aid of the machines one worker can be responsible for tending the crops of a fair-sized farm, and he can do the job efficiently. But under the old farming when man and horse were the only means of power the farmer employed most of his men to do these jobs, and in addition he hired women and children to do some of the work at this season.

But first he harrowed the young corn. The harrow treated the tender plants roughly, snatching off some of the blades of the young wheat, for instance; but the crop quickly recovered and branched or *tillered* more strongly. The harrow also stirred up the soil between the *ringes* or rows of corn, killing the young weeds that were just beginning to form. Before the appearance of the corn shoots the farmer employed children, both girls and boys, to scare off the birds: in October and November to guard the winter corn, in March and April to watch over the spring sowing. Many of the old people who did this job sixty and seventy years ago told me some of their experiences. They called the job *crow-keeping*, a phrase that

54

Shakespeare used to describe it; some called it *bird-keeping* or *bird-tending*—keeping the birds off the newly sown land—while others referred to it simply as *rook-scaring*. But whatever birds were warned off, the method of doing it was very much the same in the whole of East Anglia. As soon as it was light the farmer sent the child out into the fields; and there the child remained while it was still light. Mrs Celia Jay (born 1883) of Blaxhall gave me an account of how she went crow-keeping at the end of last century:

10.
Bird-scaring
clappers

'My father was a shepherd for Mr John Goddard of Tunstall; and I would go out to scare rooks and crows on Mr Goddard's fields. My father made me a pair of wooden clappers and I used to rattle these and call out:

> *Cadows and crows,*
> *Take care of your toes.*
> *For here come my clappers*
> *To knock you down back'uds.*
> *Holla ca-whoo! Ca-whoo!*
>
> *Here come a stone*
> *To break your back-bone:*
> *Here come the farmer with his big gun*
> *And you must fly and I must run.*
> *Holla ca-whoo! Ca-whoo!*

[Cadows are jackdaws, a word used by Thomas Tusser in the sixteenth century.]

'It was very lonely work, and I was often perished with cold before the end of the day. If I stopped making a noise, someone from the farm would soon be along to see what I was doing.'

A contemporary of Mrs Jay, Dan Pilgrim of Helmingham (born 1882), remembers one of his first jobs on the farm after he left school at the age of twelve. The farmer sent him to keep a flock of larks off a field that had just been set with winter corn: 'It was late November or early December; and when it got dark about half-past four time I made my way back to the farm thinking my job was done. But the foreman sent me back, although it was already too dark to see the field let alone the larks. He wanted me to stay up in there until half-past five—knocking off time. I started back to the field but I fetched on round and went home instead.'

In the log-books kept by East Anglian schoolmasters of this period there are many entries referring to *bird-keeping*. The log-book is a day-to-day record of anything noteworthy that occurs concerning a school; and at this time *field-work* was often referred to. The head-teachers of Helmingham school made many entries such as this: *Many absent; working in the fields*. Field-work caused a perpetual conflict between the head-master and the parents; and it was one of those differences about which there was much to be said on both sides. Since the Education Act of 1871 parents had been made responsible for ensuring that their children got a proper schooling, but they had to pay a penny or twopence a week for each child who attended school and often a few pence for the slate and the pencil the child used to write his lessons. It was not until 21st September, 1891, that the Helmingham schoolmaster, Henry Orchard, was able to write in his log-book:

'*Free grant conditions*: this school has become free throughout, both as regards fees and books.'

A few months before this, in June, he had written: 'All the children are progressing favourably with their work except a few families who will not attend regularly: the W's the A's and the Y's are the worst offenders. These renounce the Attendance

Officer and all his ways. Notices from me go in the fire. Compulsory attendance in the country is a farce.'

But making education absolutely free did not ease the schoolmaster's job, as he soon found out, or better the condition of country parents to any extent. For during the whole of the last quarter of the nineteenth century and for the first part of this, farming depressions followed one another with disastrous regularity. Labour was plentiful. Many men were unemployed, therefore labour was cheap and wages very low. A farm-worker during the 'nineties in Suffolk got a weekly wage of between ten and eleven shillings, but only if he worked a full week. If the weather was too wet for field-work the farmer often sent his *day-men* home and they got nothing for the days they had lost. (The term day-man, or day-labourer showed that they were hired by the day.)

Under these conditions parents with large families—and most families were large at that time—wanted their children to earn as much money as they could to help pay for their keep. The farmers, too, wanted to employ children because their labour was cheaper; and wherever they could they employed them on seasonal jobs on the farm, often when the children were supposed to be at school. The school authorities were thus working against intense social pressure, and their task was a hard one. Nowhere is this more clear than in regard to one of the jobs in the field, a job that boys and girls—and their mothers—hated most of all but which they were compelled to do because of their need to get more money to live.

This was stone-picking. Briefly, it meant gathering stones off the field in a bucket and carrying it to a heap which was later picked up by one of the farmer's men who carried the stones away in a tumbril. The stone-pickers were paid by the bushel. The job was usually carried on in early spring not so much because the crops or their manner of cultivation needed it but because in East Anglia, where there is little natural rock or stone, the flints from the fields were required to make road surfaces. Selling their stone to the County Council, who were

responsible for the roads' upkeep, was a source of income to
the farmers. But the practice had gone on for centuries long
before county councils existed. It was the duty of one of the
old parish officers, the Overseer of the Highways, to see that
the roads in his parish were usable; and Thomas Tusser revealed that children went stone-picking over 400 years ago:

> *Let children be hired to lay to their bones*
> *from fallow, as needeth, to gather up stones.*
> (May Husbandry)

But during the last century it was from the growing corn that
the children picked stones, and not particularly from the fallow
land as Tusser advised. They did their work, too, earlier in
the year when it was even more unpleasant through the cold-
ness of the season. The Helmingham school log-book tells the
story of the continual battle of an enlightened headmaster,
Henry Orchard, to keep children in school when outside
pressures conspired to keep up the old custom:

'*22nd March, 1878*: Fine weather and fair attendance. Eliza
Theobald went home without leave this afternoon. Many
children applied for leave to go stone-picking—not granted.'

Again in '*April, 1890*: Farmers have a great wish to employ
children at stone-picking, but so far I have prevented many,
except those above the 4th standard, from joining a gang.'

About this time the Government set up a Commission to
inquire into the depressed condition of farming: the Commis-
sioner, A. Wilson Fox, made his report in 1893. He, too, like
the schoolmaster appears to have had some doubts about the
gang-system, whereby one man, the gang-master, contracted
with a farmer to hire labour and pick the stones from his field.
Wilson Fox visited two areas in Norfolk and Suffolk and he
quoted evidence about gangs from a Norfolk farm-worker:

'Statement by William Bensley, August 9th, 1892:

'I am 21 years of age. I began work with the gangs after I
left school at 13 years of age, and worked for three years.

'In Swaffham there are three gangs. One is a woman's gang,

which consists of girls and some married women, about 20 in all.

'There are two boys' gangs about 25 in each.

'When I first joined the gang, I earned 8d a day. I daresay the farmer paid the gang-master 1s a day for my work. When I was 16 I earned 10d a day. We began to work in the summer at 8 a.m., and left off at 5 p.m., with an hour for dinner between 12 and 1.

'In the winter we worked from 8 a.m. to 3 p.m., and half an hour or three-quarters off for dinner. When working with a gang one would work much harder than at day work.

'No boys over 20 with the gangs now.

'We would walk 2 or 2½ miles to our work, but if we had to go further than that, the farmer would meet us and drive us.

'I think the gangs are demoralizing. They teach the boys bad habits and bad language, but I think a great deal depends on the gang-master.

'If the one I was with heard bad language, he would try and stop it.

'The work with the gangs is casual. Sometimes I used to work less than three days a week; some weeks I would work every day. I think gangs are good in this way, that they teach the boys when young to do their work properly.'

But to return to Helmingham: the schoolmaster could see that whatever the force of the arguments put forward—the parents and the farmers on one side, the teachers and the school authorities on the other—the children were being exploited. And many people outside shared his views. But on 30th March, 1899, he wrote:

'Closed for a fortnight. This is in accordance with the resolution passed by the [school] Managers so as to give the children an opportunity of stone-picking.'

As many of the school managers were themselves farmers, we can readily understand the unequal pressure brought on the school and the children.

The Growing Corn

Henry Orchard's successor at Helmingham, Charles Thompson (born 1883) took up his job as headteacher in September, 1915, and almost immediately after his appointment he came up against this problem of 'school or field-work?' This was in connection with the so-called Labour Certificate. In order to lessen the conflict between keeping a child at school until he was fourteen and the need for him to become a bread-winner, the Government had passed a law (in 1876) stating that a child should be issued with a Labour Certificate as soon as he gained a certain standard in his school subjects. This enabled a bright child to leave school at twelve or even eleven years of age. Many of the men and women I talked to left Helmingham school before reaching fourteen. But in 1915, in Charles Thompson's first year, all those children who sat for their Labour Certificate failed to get it. But the new headmaster agreed with the schools inspector who had come out to examine them: their failure was by no means a disaster as it would enable the children to stay longer at school and thus defer starting work until they were bigger and better equipped to do so.

SOURCES AND BOOKS FOR FURTHER READING

A. WILSON FOX. *The Agricultural Labourer* (Vol. 1, Part 3 England) H.M.S.O., 1893
Helmingham School Log Books, 1863–1931
RICHARD HILLYER. *Country Boy*, Hodder & Stoughton, 1966
Ask the Fellows Who Cut the Hay

6

The Harvest

The conflict in the countryside between school and work ceased in August and early September; and it gives us some idea of the importance of the old corn harvest to notice that the school summer holidays were always known as *Harvest* holidays. For harvest took precedence over everything else: so important was it that there was no debate about bringing the school holidays forward if the corn ripened early or extending them if the harvest was late.

It is hard for us to realize today what an occasion the corn harvest was under the old system of farming. It was the climax of the year; and, indeed, the rural year ended at Michaelmas (29th September) by which time the corn was usually gathered in. Most people in the village were involved, either directly or indirectly, and there was work for all. Moreover, the work at harvest was on a different basis from most work during the rest of the farming year. Harvest was piece-work, *taken* work, let out on contract by the farmer who bargained with the workmen who were represented by their *Lord of the Harvest*. The agreement was to win the harvest during a certain period of about a month or '28 fine days' for a certain price—usually about double the normal wage for this time. The prosperity of the farmer and his workers depended upon whether or not they got a good harvest: a bad harvest meant disaster for the farmer and indirectly for the workmen whose hope of employment for the ensuing year lessened while at the same time the price of grain—and therefore the price of bread—rose with its scarcity.

George Rope (1814–1912), the nineteenth-century farmer, recorded some of these bad harvests in his Blaxhall diaries. The harvest of 1860 was a particularly bad one:

'The wettest and coldest summer to this time [15th August] I ever remember. The corn ripens very slowly. I am told that a large quantity of wheat in Yorkshire and northward of that County is not yet in ear. The wheat and barley on the mixsoil lands, well manured, promise exceedingly well, but on the cold clays and wet lands the barley crop will be very bad; thousands of acres in Suffolk will not produce 3 coombs pr. acre and a large portion will not pay for harvesting. The pea crop promised well but there being so much straw the continual wet weather has rotted the straw before the peas were ripe and the earliest pods have burst by the swelling of the peas so that instead of a large crop of that grain it will be a small one and inferior quality.

'Began making up peas today (13 Aug.), the first fine day for some time. I think I may venture to say two thirds of the hay is spoiled.'

George Rope also recorded the weather for the notoriously bad year 1879—*Black '79*; and the equally disastrous one for 1894, which followed, ironically, Wilson Fox's report on the low condition of farming. These last two bad harvests are in the memory of people still living and they are often talked about in the corn areas. These bad years were also logged by the Helmingham schoolmaster as the weather and the state of the harvest closely affected school attendance:

September 22nd, 1879: Reopened school; very bad attendance owing to harvest being delayed by the bad weather.

' *"23rd–24th;* Very wet. School closed on account of heavy flood and rain.'

But modern developments have changed the direct dependence of a locality on its own harvests. Mechanization and modern transport have opened up the world and made it one huge market. As Lord Ernle wrote in his famous *English Farming Past and Present*: 'Instead of there being one harvest every year, there is now a harvest every month.' If the local harvest fails, disaster is not as widespread—at least few need go hungry for this reason as at one time they used to. Neither are the people of a rural community so directly involved in harvest as they were. Someone living in a village today may watch with interest the progress of the farming year, particularly in a field, for instance, which lies near his house. He may carefully observe the ploughing of the previous year's stubble, the harrowing and the rolling, the drilling of the corn, the spraying, and the growth of the crop from the stage of a faint green *cast* to an undulating sea of lusty corn. Yet if he happens to be away from home for a day, or perhaps even an afternoon, he may miss the actual harvest altogether. While he was in the town two men and a combine harvester have reaped the corn and left neat, parallel lines of straw refuse behind them. But this is not to say that substituting the work of the machine for the sweat and the slavery of the old sickle and scythe harvest which went out at the beginning of the century is a bad development. In the following pages I wish merely to record, with reference to harvest, that its mechanization meant not only a basic change in technique but the end of a kind of society that was in continuous line with those early farmers who gathered their corn in essentially the same manner before the Romans set foot in these islands.

After the *haysel*, the time of the hay-harvest (O.E. *sael*: time or season), came the *barleysel*, the harvesting of the barley which was the typical corn crop in East Anglia in Anglo-Saxon times, as it is in parts of the region today. The harvest at that time was a season of intense activity and excitement because it meant that the whole community was ensuring its means of living over the coming winter into the next harvest. Early farming—farming to live or subsist—gave this plenty-or-hunger edge to the gathering of the crop; and up to this century this excitement, merriment, and thankfulness remained

11. Corn dolly (Mother Earth)

for long after the time when the success of the home harvests ceased to be as critical as they once were.

Sir John Cullum in his *History of Hawsted* gave an account of how the harvest was conducted in the fourteenth century.

On the manor of Hawstead, Suffolk, in the year 1388, 553 persons were employed in the harvest; and 520 in the following year. This was not including the baker, cook and brewer who catered for this small army of workers. Harvest at that time certainly involved 'a fair field full of folk' as the poet Langland wrote, because the annual number of acres of all sorts of corn sown at Hawstead did not much exceed 200. It is clear that the aim was to get the corn in as quickly as possible. Two large parties of workers were hired every year for one day each, and it is probable that they finished the harvest in two days.

5. TUCK'S MILL, BADINGHAM (SUFFOLK). Burnt down *c.* 1916

6. MARLESFORD HALL FARM
(SUFFOLK) *c.* 1916

7. SHARMAN'S MILL, RISHANGLES
(SUFFOLK). Burnt down 1904

Writing at the end of the eighteenth century Sir John Cullum observed: 'And these [two] days were perhaps at some distance from each other, as all the different sorts of corn were scarcely ripe at the same time. Yet I know not, if the object was to finish the general harvest in two or three days, whether all the crops might not be sown so as to be all fit to be cut at once. The farmers at present [*c.* 1784] sow their different grains with a view to a harvest of about five weeks' continuance.' If the harvest was actually completed in two or three days (and the hiring of 44 pitchers, stackers and reapers, a 1389 entry, seems to suggest that it was) the sheaves of corn were not left in the field in stooks as they were in modern times but gathered immediately. This may be the explanation of the *Luttrell Psalter* illustration where the sheaves are being piled together in a rough kind of stack; ready presumably for carting.

Again, we would be safe in assuming that some of the harvest workers worked on more than one manor, taking part in more than one harvest. Itinerant harvesters were not unknown in East Anglia at the beginning of this century. Occasionally a Suffolk man first did a harvest in Essex where it was often gathered slightly earlier than in Suffolk. He then returned to his own district; did another harvest there, and was sometimes able to get a later harvest still in Norfolk. Itinerant Irish workers were well known in the harvests in the north of England and in Scotland. But it is likely that this fourteenth-century harvest at Hawstead was a kind of communal harvest, similar to the ones that persisted in the hay-harvest in parts of Wales until recent years. Instead of each farmer harvesting his own hay with his own labour force, farmers grouped together and harvested each farm's crop in rotation. And here, just as on the fourteenth-century Suffolk manor, there was communal catering, only on a very much smaller scale. One entry for the 1389 harvest at Hawstead confirms that there was at least some voluntary help. Sir John Cullum has translated it: '22 reapers hired for the day for good will (*de amore*)'—a surprising proof of the age of the modern slang phrase 'for love'.

The Harvest

Here are some of the items listed in the Hawstead rolls for
the 1388 harvest: the expenses for a ploughman, head-reaper,
baker, cook, brewer, deye (a day labourer, possibly in the
dairy) and 244½ reapers hired for one day. There were also 30
bedrepes, or days of work performed at harvest time by the
customary tenants of the man or 'at the bidding or requisition
of their lord'. The main food of the harvest workers was bread
and herrings, their drink beer. They consumed in one day:

3 quarters, 3 bushels of wheat from the stock	
5 quarters, 3 bushels of malt	
Meat bought	10s 10d
5 sheep from the stock	
Fish and Herrings bought	5s 0d
Herrings for the customary tenants	7d
Cheese, milk and butter bought	9s 6d
Salt	3d

The steward also paid out 5d for candles, and 5d for spoons,
dishes and faucets (wooden taps for ale-casks), a comparatively
small amount but paid probably for replacements.

The entry '244½ reapers' may seem strange but the '½' refers
to a lad who was not able to do the work of a man. This
designation lasted in Suffolk until a few years ago. A lad went
into the harvest contract as a 'half-man' and he was paid accordingly. There was also a 'three-quarter man' in some villages up

12.
Sheaf of wheat
with straw-band

to the First World War (see *Ask the Fellows who Cut the Hay*, Chapter ₁11): he was a lad who had almost reached his full strength and could do the work of a full man except pitching, the heavy work of handling the sheaves of corn on to the wagon.

The Hawstead accounts have an item '5 pairs of gloves, 10d'. We have already mentioned gloves for the weeders, a use which is confirmed by the *Luttrell Psalter* illustration of a man weeding, as well as by Tusser. The inclusion of gloves in the harvesting expenses is explained by the need for protection while handling the corn, since many thistles still remained in it in spite of the most careful weeding. But gloves were also used ceremonially at harvest as we know from Tusser:

'Give gloves to thy reapers a largesse to cry.'

Crying largesse was a ceremony which Suffolk reapers took part in on the harvest field up to the end of the last century. But there is no evidence that they wore gloves specially for this. Sir John Cullum quotes two instances which suggest this ceremonial use: the monastery at Bury St Edmunds allowed several of its servants 2d a-piece for *glove-silver*; and an account of Elizabeth I's entertainment at Kenilworth Castle in 1575 where the rural bridegroom 'had a payr of harvest gloves on his hands as a sign of good husbandry'.

The great band of Hawstead reapers was supervised by the head-reaper (*super-messor* or *prae-positus*). On the manor he was elected and presented by the lord to the inhabitants. During the year he served he was exempt from all or half his rent or dues and he had numerous privileges including sitting at the lord's table and putting up his horse in the manorial stables. Getting in the harvest quickly and efficiently was like a military operation, and the Lord of the Harvest—as Tusser called him—was like a battle commander and he summoned up the reapers with the aid of a horn in real army fashion. An illuminated manuscript of this time shows the Lord using the harvest horn in the field.

This medieval organization of the harvest lasted in East Anglia until the break-up of the old farming régime. The farm-workers elected a Lord who was usually the head-horseman or foreman on the farm, and the Lord in turn chose a deputy who was called his Lady. Between them they took absolute charge while the season of harvest lasted; and the farmer stood on one side. The Lord was the man who led the line of reapers in the field, who set the pace, the rest keeping in echelon behind him. He, too, was the man who was left to estimate the size of the corn stack, who saw to it that the sheaves of corn were properly laid in the stack and that it would rise up straight and stand in good order against wind and weather until the time of threshing—a task and a responsibility that befitted a leader.

But the Lord's first duty was to bargain with the farmer about the rate that he and his band were to be paid during harvest. After they had come to an agreement the farmer pronounced the usual words: 'I'll put it [the harvest] out to you.' And the Lord replied according to the formula: 'I'll take it,' thus sealing the bargain. The procedure was called *taking the harvest*, and was normally held as a little ceremony in the farmer's house. After this the men, in command of their chosen Lord, were more or less on their own.

This feeling of managing their own affairs, if only for a brief time, gave the harvest a special atmosphere that was different

13. Costrel and tot (for drinks in harvest field)

from the rest of the year. The men enjoyed it in spite of the
back-breaking work that—on most days—lasted from early
morning until late evening, because they felt that here they were
all on the same footing; and the man who went out in front
did so not because of any given privilege but by virtue of his
own skill and endurance in the day-long toil in the field. The
words the Suffolk poet, Robert Bloomfield, wrote in his
Farmer's Boy about the harvest feast, the *horkey* or *frolic*, could
as well be applied to the whole exercise:

> *Here once a year Distinction low'rs its crest;*
> *The master, servant, and the merry guest*
> *Are equal all.*

The farmer usually made a copy of the harvest agreement;
and here is one George Rope, the Blaxhall farmer, drew up for
six of his men. They were to harvest the wheat at 8s od an
acre; the barley, peas, and turnips at 7s od per acre (the turnips
had to be hoed twice during the time of the contract); and the
men were granted certain allowances:

> 1 coomb wheat at 20s
> 3 lb mutton at 4d
> 3 bushels of malt, given
> 1 stone of mutton, instead of dinners
> ½ pint of best beer in the morning and
> 1 pint in the afternoon when after the corn
> Hiring money—1s each
> Wetting Do.

If we compare these allowances with the Hawstead list of
food and drink consumed at harvest we can see how little
harvest-fare in Suffolk had changed in 500 years.

The Blaxhall men were allowed the comb of wheat at this
special rate to go with the comb or two of wheat that would be
won by their wives and children at the gleaning. This wheat
was then ground at Blaxhall mill, and the flour baked at home
into bread. The beer given to the workmen at harvest was

made at Grove Farm, for which this contract was drawn up. It was a special harvest brew and was made by the head horseman. The best beer was called *Key Beer* because it was kept under lock and key to prevent anyone making the very natural mistake of broaching the wrong cask. The copper vessel, called a *ranter*, in which the beer was carried on to the field at this time, still survives. *Hiring money*, sometimes called *earnest money*, was the shilling given by the farmer to each man as an earnest that the bargain was sealed. *Wetting money* refers also to the same custom—the ceremonial drink called *Wetting the Sickle* to conclude the proceedings. In this particular contract the actual drink appears to have been commuted for a money payment.

A description of the other customs connected with the corn harvest are to be found in the book about Blaxhall, *Ask the Fellows who Cut the Hay*; but we can here again emphasize their age by referring to Thomas Tusser whose *August Husbandry* lists many of the customs which were preserved right up to the First World War; and he also refers to the 'turning of peason' and 'the stacking of pease upon hovell', both of which processes figured many times in George Rope's harvest contracts, giving them a continuity of at least four centuries.

On the Helmingham estate each allotment holder had his little harvest; and a description of the process on these miniature farms reflects what happened on the large farms themselves many years earlier. The half-acre of land, ideally in a rectangular strip at the back of the cottage, was divided by a central path. The cottage dweller planted vegetables on one side of the path and corn on the other; and he alternated the crop—corn on the right of the path one year, on the left during the next. Caleb Howe of Framsden used to dig over the whole of his allotment with a spade, having first spread manure from the pigs he kept in the top corner of his piece of land. He got straw-bedding for his pigs free from the farm where he worked: in return he let the farmer cart away to the fields all the manure he did not want. He planted his wheat with dibbles—*debbled it*, as he said. But later: 'I made a wooden frame with five *counters* [coulters: he called the frame his *marker*]. We dragged this across the land, and it made five *ringes* [small grooves or furrows] as it went. Then we dropped the seed into the ringes, and raked it over. Later on I gave this up and when Mr Thompson got his drill, I borrowed that every year. Joe Thompson's drill got about the country a lot: he's still got it I believe.

'I harvested my corn with the sickle at first, then with the reap-hook or the bagging iron—the *bagger* we used to call it.

14. Wheelbarrow (small farmers were sometimes referred to as 'wheelbarrow farmers')

With a good bagger you cut the corn so two armfuls would make a *shuff* [sheaf]. If we'd had plenty of straw from the farm we cut the corn very high, and left the straw standing nearly a cubit high. Then we *hammed* it [haulmed it: cut the straw with a scythe] and burned it on the land, as the farmers do today with most of the straw left after the combine harvester. The *shuff* was all ears you could say.

'After we got the corn in we thrashed it as soon as we got a chance. We put down a big *tilt* [tarpaulin] and we knocked out the corn on this with a flail. This was in my father's time when I were quite young, about seventy year ago. Later on we used to stack our corn out there in front by the road, just near the gate. Then a wagon came from the farm and took your small stack up there; and they threshed the corn out with the drum.

'At that time o' day if you walked down the road you'd see a little stack of wheat at nearly every gate, waiting to be taken up to one of the farms.'

William Sherman (born 1902) of Helmingham, a neighbour of Caleb Howe, added a note about the small stacks of corn which were taken to the farms to wait until the threshing drum and engine came round: 'The farmer used to stack all the men's wheat into one big stack. Each man kept his own corn separate by making a sort of dividing compartment of straw. So when it came to the threshing you knew exactly when your corn went into the drum. You'd bag that up and take it down home and store it there until it was time for it to go up to Framsden mill to be ground into flour.'

Caleb Howe got a yield of about 2½ combs of wheat from his quarter-acre, a good average yield which compared well with the farmer's:

'With the 2½ coombs of wheat went all the wheat that my mother and us children got from the gleaning. Sometimes we got as much wheat from the gleaning—as much as we'd harvested. We took the corn to Framsden mill [a post-mill, a few hundred yards from his home] and got it ground into flour. The miller, Mr Webster, used to charge us from 2s od to 2s 6d a coomb for grinding the corn. But we got the offal as well as the flour, and the best *middlings* we fed to the pigs.

'All that is done away with now. But I used the flail last autumn [1964] to thrash out some broad beans I grew; and I sold most of them in Ipswich. But the old methods have gone. Money and two Big Wars have killed 'em.'

The last comment of Caleb Howe is an acute and accurate one. The change from subsistence farming to farming solely for the market, where farm produce is grown chiefly as crops to be exchanged for cash, was a long process which took many centuries. But this system could not develop until there was one, almost magical commodity, *money*, that was recognized as the common medium and could be exchanged for all other commodities. Yet even when the market had gained its modern

72

sophistication, the old subsistence ideal (growing for direct use and not so much for profit) still existed here and there on the margin. But the two major wars of this century did away with all that. The money economy got into the saddle and trod out the vestiges of subsistence farming from such areas as Helmingham: at the same time it put an end to customs, practices, and a way of life that were as old as history. To give one concrete example: the Helmingham smallholders—as already hinted—would have a lively understanding of the Biblical harvests they heard about. *Thrust in the sickle and reap, for the time of the harvest is at hand* was an accurate description of what they did at this time, something which helped to give meaning to their lives; an activity for which they used the same implements and roughly the same methods. Even the children could fill in some of the Old Testament stories—like the story of Naomi and Ruth—with details from their own recent experience.

SOURCES AND BOOKS FOR FURTHER READING

ADRIAN BELL. *Corduroy*. Country Book Club, 1951
SUFFOLK RECORDS SOCIETY. *Suffolk Farming in the Nineteenth Century*. Ipswich, 1958
ROBERT BLOOMFIELD. *The Farmer's Boy*. London, 1803
ARTHUR RANDALL. *Sixty Years a Fenman*. Routledge, 1966
HUGH BARRETT. *Early to Rise*. Faber and Faber, 1967

The Tools of Harvest

The sickle is one of the oldest surviving implements in farming, and is still used in Suffolk—in the Bures district—but for harvesting thyme for seed and not for corn. The earliest farmers fashioned the first sickles out of pieces of sharp flint fixed in a curved bone or piece of wood. Later the sickle was made from metal with a saw-edged or serrated blade. The reaper cut the corn by bending over and grasping a bunch of ears in his left hand, as Caleb Howe did on his allotment, inserting the sickle and drawing it towards him in a sawing action. This was essentially a gentle action and it ensured that as little corn as possible would be shed and lost on the ground. The sickle lasted for so long as a harvesting tool for this very reason: it was still used in preference to the swap-hook and scythe in some areas because its use, although slower, conserved the grain.

Frank Bloomfield (born 1888) worked most of his life with Ransome, Sims and Jefferies the famous Ipswich firm of agricultural engineers; and he gave me a very modern illustration of this quality of a serrated edge. When his firm first experimented with making a combine harvester, the blades they used on the cutter were smooth-edged like the swap-hook, or scythe, or the blades on a reaper-binder. But they found that a tremendous amount of grain was lost by being shed on to the stubble. The firm then experimented by making one side

The Tools of Harvest

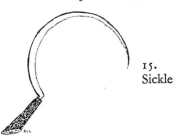

15.
Sickle

of the cutting knives with serrated edges, leaving the other smooth-edged. This improved the performance of the combine harvester slightly; but it was not until they had made serrated edges on all the knives that the loss of grain lessened appreciably. Thus the wheel has come full circle: the main feature in the design of the primitive sickle is included—much to its advantage—in the latest models of the combine harvester.

An old shepherd, Harry Mason (1876–1963), confirmed this shedding of the corn by the first combines: 'I used to turn my sheep out on to the corn stubble. We called it *shacking* [feeding on the corn that had been *shacked* or shaken out of the ear during harvest]. This was quite straight-forward when they scythed the corn or used the self-binder: I could leave the sheep in the stubble for the best part of the day and I needn't worry much about them. But as soon as the combine came in I had to be very careful with them. They picked up so much more corn that—if I were to leave them—they'd have been in trouble in no time. They would be on their backs, legs in the air and their bellies all blown up. They'd get so much grain and they'd eat it so quickly that it swelled out before they had time to digest it. It was very easy to lose sheep like that. So after the combine had been I used to open the two gates to the field; let 'em in through one and drive 'em almost straight away out through the other.'

But the design of the old, serrated sickle was also outstanding in another way: it was light and could be used all day, even by women, without the reaper tiring unduly. The curve of the blade contributed greatly to this, as Henry Stephens showed in his *Book of the Farm*. Its long use down the ages had evolved the sickle's peculiar sweeping curve which gave the tool perfect balance, ensuring that it would need the minimum effort for its use. Stephens called it *the curve of least exertion*, a design that was mathematically perfect for the use to which it was put.

There were other reasons for the long use of the sickle. 'With it,' as Caleb Howe stated, 'you could cut your corn high. You couldn't do that with the scythe.' It was light enough for a woman to use; the scythe was a different matter. Lastly the serrated blade of the sickle required no sharpening: it would last for a whole harvest without attention. Therefore, although it was a little slower in use, no time was lost in the field through frequent breaks for sharpening with the rub-stone as were needed with both swap-hook and scythe.

The scythe was originally used for mowing grass and appears to have come into general use for the corn harvest during the latter half of the nineteenth century—at least in East Anglia. But it had a special fitment called a *cradle* which helped to lay the corn in neat swathes ready to be tied up in sheaves. A corn-cradle, either of wood or metal, was fitted to the scythe-stick when wheat was being cut; a curve of hazel or bramble branch or sometimes a metal bow was fixed when harvesting barley. This was called a *barley-bale*.

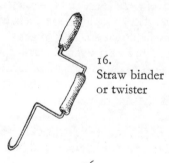

16.
Straw binder
or twister

The Tools of Harvest

Tusser in his verses cataloguing *Husbandly Furniture*, all the gear used on the farms of East Anglia during the sixteenth century and—we can surmise—for centuries afterwards, mentions the cradle to be used for barley. This is most probably the barley-bale. Incidentally, there is hardly a tool in Tusser's list that was not used or known by the old East Anglian farmworkers who are now in their late seventies or eighties. Tusser does not, however, mention the horn-mug or beaker taken by most harvest-workers into the field to hold drink to refresh themselves. But Dorothy Hartley, Tusser's editor, includes some sixteenth-century verses which reveal another instance of this remarkable continuity in the use of farming gear down the centuries. As the verses say, glasses and pots were no use on the harvest field. That is the reason why the unbreakable horn-beaker was preferred until recent years. The old leather-jack did not last as long but was displaced by the copper ranter and the heavy earthenware jug. But again as the verses say, it often appeared on the harvest field in another guise. One side of the old leather-bottle was cut out to make a receptacle for any odds-and-ends that might be needed: grass-nails for the scythes, thongs or a *false-link* for the horse-chains. I have seen two of these ancient bottles cut for this purpose in East Anglia—one here in Helmingham. But here are the verses, printed at Holborn in 1560:

Tankard and Jack

A Leather Bottel he know is good
Far better than glasses or cans of wood,
For when a Man is at work in the Field,
Your Glasses and Pots no comfort will yield,
Then a good Leather Bottel standing him by
He may drink always when he is dry.

When this bottel doth grow old,
And will good Liquor no longer hold,

The Tools of Harvest

Out of the side you may take a clout
Will mend your shoes when there worn out,
Else take it and hang it upon a pin,
It will serve to put odd trifles in,
As hinges, awls and candle ends,
For young Beginners must have such thinges.

Then I wish in Heaven his soul may dwell
That first devised the Leather Bottel!

In George Rope's harvest contract (page 69) he included the rate for harvesting peas. The peas had to be cut, turned (twice usually), and carted. The tool used for cutting the peas was called a pea-make: it is a steel blade, with a shallow curve, fixed on a long handle which was invariably ash. This is the kind of implement that is always well to the fore in imaginative illustrations of medieval peasants gathering for a revolt. Tusser called it:

a meak for the pease and to swinge up the brake.

Apparently it was used at that time for cutting brakes or bracken as well as for harvesting peas.

SOURCES AND BOOKS FOR FURTHER READING

NORMAN E. LEE. *Harvests and Harvesting*

HENRY STEPHENS. *The Book of the Farm*. William Blackwood, 1877 (Third Edition)

NIGEL HARVEY. *The Story of Farm Buildings* (1953) Young Farmers' Club Booklet. Evans Brothers

HIGGS AND BEECHAM. *The Story of Farm Tools* (1961) Young Farmers' Club Booklet. Evans Brothers

THOMAS TUSSER. *His Farming in East Anglia*. Edited by Dorothy Hartley (*Country Life*, 1931)

8

After the Harvest

The Helmingham cottage holders added to the store of corn they grew on their allotments by gleaning on the fields after harvest. This was another activity that was more important than school, as the following entry in the Helmingham School log-book shows:

'*16th September, 1898*: Owing to the operations in the harvest being greatly hindered by the laid condition of the crops and consequently gleaning being behind, the Managers decided to extend the holidays another week; and the Clergy were asked to give notice to that effect in the churches.'

An earlier entry for the same year explains the expression *laid condition of the crops*. It was another wet summer:

'*10th June*: Heavy rain and flood. Did not open in the morning. Kept school for a short time in the afternoon, but owing to the water's rising so rapidly at the bridge had to dismiss the children and cancel attendances.'

As the corn was laid flat, it made scything slow and difficult work, causing the whole harvest operation to be retarded.

Celia Jay gave me an account of how she and her sister gleaned at Tunstall in Suffolk about seventy-five years ago. She had a special apron made for gleaning. In the front it had a big pocket which she called a *chob-poke* [a poke is a bag; cf. *To buy a pig in a poke*: *chobs* is the dialect word for the ears of corn]. She also carried a pair of scissors: with this she clipped the straw off the short stalks, dropping the ears into her pocket. She collected the long strawed corn and bound them into a small sheaf with a wisp of straw, exactly as she had seen her mother do when she was helping in the field binding up the corn as it was cut.

In the Blaxhall and Tunstall district earlier in last century, the sexton used to ring the church-bell at 8 o'clock in the morning as a signal that the gleaning could start in the parish. He rang it again at 7 o'clock at night to warn the gleaners that their work for that day must end. But during living memory farmers used the following practice to control the gleaning and to prevent forestalling and argument among the gleaners. After the farm-workers had cleared a field of the crop they left one sheaf standing on it. This last sheaf was called the *Policeman*, and it was understood that no gleaner could enter the field while the Policeman was on guard. As soon as the farmer took the last sheaf away the gleaners were free to enter.

The conditions of the farm-workers during the 'nineties made gleaning essential: a loss of the gleaned corn would have meant actual hunger to many a farm-worker's family during the ensuing year. This is the reason why the school authorities realized it would be useless to open school while the gleaning was still in progress.

At this time of harvest, during the carting of the corn, straw ropes were much used. These were made on the farm with the aid of an implement called a straw-rope binder. It was of a very simple design: a crank very much like a brace, but having a hook where the bit is fixed. It required two operators to make a straw rope. One turned the crank and walked backwards while the other, after looping a few wisps of straw on the hook to start it off, stood by the stack or by a heap of straw and fed the stalks into the twisting and lengthening rope.

The men carted the corn from the fields in the four-wheeled harvest wagons, and it was either stacked or went straight into the barn. Barley was the crop that was most frequently stored in the barn because in Suffolk, at least, it was always harvested and carted loose, not bound into sheaves like wheat, oats or rye. It was *gavelled* or raked into rows and then loaded on to the wagon. But if it was a very wet harvest the barley would have to be turned before carting. I was reminded of this in a conversation I had with Caleb Howe:

'One year we had to turn the barley three times for nothing [that is, it was not mentioned in the harvest contract with the farmer]. So next year when we were ready to *take the harvest*, just before we went to the farmhouse, I said to my mates— most on 'em much older men: "We can't hev that again this year. We must be paid for it. And you must stand by me when I ask." They were afraid, these older men, and they were sure

17.
Corn neck
or knack

I'd get the sack. But when we went into the house to bargain with the farmer, I asked him. He looked at me some queer as though I'd spoken out o' ma turn. But nothing happened, and we got paid for turning the barley every year after that.'

The East Anglian barns in which the corn was stored deserve very much more notice than they have been given. They were a vital part of the economy in the corn areas, a focus of much of the work. Moreover, the outstanding East Anglian barns like the Paston barn near North Walsham in Norfolk or the Framsden Hall barn in Suffolk, show how important these old farm buildings are from the standpoint of medieval architecture. Some of them are constructed very much like a church; and an Essex writer, C. Henry Warren, very aptly called them 'cathedrals of labour'. When empty the ten-bay Framsden barn, and even more so the Paston barn which is built of stone, have the same noble proportions as the nave of a great church.

But the small farm barns have usually only three bays, each about fifteen to sixteen feet across; and this too is the usual width of the actual barn itself.

Big double doors led to the central bay of the barn, the middlestead, where the threshing was later carried on. The double doors allowed the wagons loaded with corn to pass right through on to the floor of the middlestead. The men then

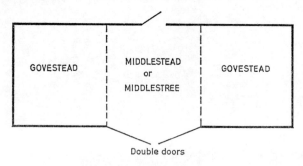

18. A three-bay corn barn

unloaded the corn into the side bays each of which was called the *gof*—or *goafstead*. Gof or gove means the corn in the ear or the *mow* or stack; that is, before it is threshed. Tusser called it the *goef*, and we can be sure that, like the word, the design of the barn itself and the work that went on in it had hardly changed from the sixteenth century to within living memory.

One practice linked with this stage of the harvest was called *riding the goaf* in Suffolk. As the loose barley was unloaded on to the goafstead, a boy rode a quiet old farmhorse round and round on the corn, trampling it down. The main purpose was to pack as much corn as possible into the bay; but in treading the corn in this way much of it was shaken out of the ear, and thus a start was made on the threshing. Many of the older Suffolk farm-workers, now long retired, remember riding the goaf as lads; and they have described how they rose higher and higher on the mow as it increased in depth. The problem came when horse and rider could rise no higher and had to be got down. One man told me that they left a rough sort of ramp at one side of the corn, and the horse slid down this on to the middlestead. Another described how a strong rope was thrown over one of the barn's tie-beams and then fixed to the horse's harness. The men then eased him down by taking much of his weight on the rope.

Some readers have found it difficult to believe this and similar descriptions of riding the goaf; and, not having seen it done and finding it difficult to imagine how it could be done, assume it to be a piece of historical fiction that gives a little sentimental colour to the old country community. But the country tradition, where it describes the actual *work*, farming in this instance, cannot in my experience be faulted. Here is a description of the same custom as it was practised 200 years ago on a farm at Sapiston in West Suffolk. Robert Bloomfield, in his autobiographical poem *The Farmer's Boy*, written at the end of the eighteenth century, revealed that he had himself ridden the goaf as a small, rather undersized lad: .

After the Harvest

. . . e'en humble Giles
Who joys his service to yield
Amidst the fragrance of the open field;
Oft doom'd in suffocating heat to bear
The cob-web'd barn's impure and dusty air;
To ride in murky state the panting steed,
Destin'd aloft the unloaded grain to tread,
Where, in his path as heaps on heaps are thrown,
He rears and plunges the loose mountain down;
Laborious task! with what delight when done
Both horse and rider greet the unclouded sun.

Later in the year, after the winter corn had been sown and the bad weather had set in, the farmer had his men go to the barn to thresh out the corn. The flail, the tool they used for this purpose, has always been as much a symbol of the corn harvest

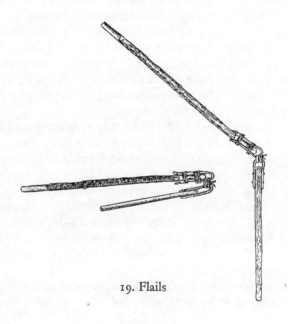

19. Flails

as the sickle itself; and its history is almost as ancient. In East Anglia its story extends from Roman times right up to the present. The flail succeeded the beating-stick and improved on its action. For the beating-stick, as it was in one piece, had to be used in a straight up-and-down action to beat out the corn. But the flail can be used in a circular action like a whip which enables its operator to keep up a steady rhythm. In fact the word flail derives from the Latin *flagellum*, a whip. The implement is basically two sticks, joined by a flexible knot. The Suffolk name for it, *a stick-and-a-half*, gives a clear picture of its proportions. The stick or handle is usually made of ash and is twice as long as the swingel, the part that strikes the straw to shake out the grain. Tusser recommended two types of tough wood for the making of a swingel:

> *Save hazel for forks, save sallow for rake;*
> *Save hulver and thorn thereof flail to make.*

The swingels of all the flails I have seen in East Anglia are made of the wood Tusser advised, either holly or blackthorn. But I have a flail here which is made from yew, a wood which is equally tough.

As suggested, the threshing was left until the bad weather when the farmer found it hard to give workers jobs to do in the field. December or the early months of the year were the threshing times; and the flail continued to be used on the farms of East Anglia long after the introduction of the threshing machines at the beginning of the nineteenth century. One of the reasons for this was the amount of seasonal unemployment among farm-workers. Rather than have a number of men in the parish living entirely on parish relief, the parish authorities arranged with the farmers to pay part of the wages of the men who were given work threshing in the barn with a flail. It was for this reason it was known as the *poverty stick* in Cambridgeshire.

But there are few men, if any, still living in East Anglia, who have used the flail for threshing corn in the barn; though there are many like the Helmingham men who have threshed corn from their own allotments. But a number of eighty-year-old farm-workers have used the flail to thresh out beans for seed. This process lasted so long because it was risky to put beans through the threshing drum to *knock them out* of the pods: the machinery injured the husks and considerably lowered the percentage of beans that would germinate.

All those who had experience of threshing with the flail agree that it was monotonous and gruelling work, only relieved by having company—five or six men threshing on the middlestead at a time. To break the monotony they resorted to many devices. One of these was to keep a certain pre-arranged rhythm, and as we have seen the design of the flail lends itself to this. In the Suffolk village of Barking those threshers who were also bell-ringers went on to the threshing floor together—perhaps half a dozen at a time; and they used the same rhythm while threshing as they used in the steeple when ringing the bells. As they were *change-ringers* some of the rhythms were exceedingly subtle. Most middlesteads were floored with elm or poplar before the coming of the machines (nearly all have since been concreted) and the threshing rhythm could be heard some distance from the barn. I was reminded of this practice and of the subtlety of the rhythms and the way they helped the work along when I talked to William Manning (born 1894) of Helmingham: he had threshed rye in Germany over 50 years ago. It happened in this way:

'During the First World War I was on the Western Front—on the Somme; and in the summer of 1916 we made a dawn attack—4 o'clock in the morning. But it didn't come off, and I and about sixty others were captured. They took us to Germany, and before long I found myself working on a farm in Westphalia. Well, I didn't know Sunday from a weekday in Germany; but I knew their farming. It weren't no different from the farming in Suffolk—except they grew a lot of rye and they drove their plough horses with one rein (they had a young 'un and an old 'un together and they tied the young 'un to

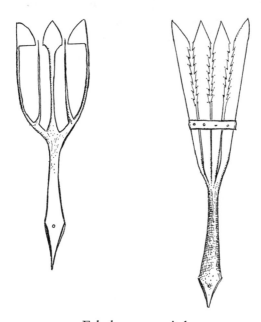

20. Eel-glaves or -pritches

the other so he could guide him). They cut the corn with the
scythe and cradle; and, here and there, with the self-binder—
everything the same. The barns were the same and they did
their threshing in the barn just as I'd done myself over here
before going into the army. Almost as soon as I got there they
found me a job threshing with a flail—in a barn with five oldish
women, between 60 and 70 years of age. But, do you know,
they had a sort of rhythm of their own, and I just couldn't fit
in with it. And of course I couldn't speak the language; so I
couldn't get on with the threshing. I soon got them to put me
on to something else.'

C. Henry Warren in one of his books gave another sidelight
on the rhythm of threshing with the flail. He wrote that in parts
of Essex the villagers could tell by the rhythm on what terms a
threshing party had been engaged, on *piece-* or *taken-work*, or

just ordinary *day-work*. If the latter, then the swing of the flails made a succession of slow spondees: *By—t h e—d a y. By— t h e—d a y.* But if it was *taken-work* the rhythm was as lively as a country jig: *We-took-it. We-took-it. We-took-it.*

Another device used by the threshers in Suffolk to help break up the hard grind of flail-thrashing was the holding of a kind of competition. Each thresher while working held a six-inch straw in his mouth; and the test of skill was to get the swingel to touch the straw each time it came down in its stroke to beat the corn. As the swingel is fixed to the stick so that it swings in almost any direction, it was very easy for anyone except a skilled man to do injury to his head or his face when taking part in this exercise. The flail was, in fact, the first universal joint—a joint that will allow movement in any direction. A good flail has a kind of ball-and-socket arrange-ment with a cap fitted at the top of the stick. The cap is usually made of sweated yew, and the loop of the wooden cap is tied to the swingel by a loose but intricate knot, made from whit-leather, tough pigskin, or—as often in earlier days in East Anglia—eelskin. Many workers made their own flails; but there was in later years a manufactured kind that could be bought in the ironmonger's shop as could most of the other hand-tools used in farming.

While the men were threshing, grain invariably got into their boots. One of the famous types of barley used in the nineteenth century in Britain, and also in North America—Chevallier barley—was evolved out of the few grains a farm-worker at Debenham in Suffolk brought home in his boots after thresh-ing. But undoubtedly many farm-workers with not too nice a conscience used to ensure that before going home their boots would have very much more corn in them than they had acquired in the normal course of threshing. Many farmers were alive to this and they insisted that their threshers should empty their boots before leaving the threshing floor. The farmers knew that chickens were fed on corn and that corn was often planted in allotments. Tusser also knew of this tendency among threshers to walk away with corn either for seed or food for their stock:

> *Some pilfering thresher will walk with a staff ;*
> *will carry home corn as it is in the chaff.*
> *And some in his bottle of leather so great*
> *Will carry home daily both barley and wheat.*

This practice and the precaution against it have survived in East Anglia up to the present. A year or two ago one Suffolk fruit-farmer would not allow anyone picking small fruit—black-currants and so on—on his farm to bring any drink receptacle to work except a clear glass one.

This verse also emphasizes in another way how little farming and the life connected with it had changed between the late Middle Ages and the recent past: wheat is still pronounced *whate* in East Anglian dialect, to rhyme with *great* exactly as it did in Tusser's day.

The fear that farm-workers would pilfer corn and meal was much wider than one would imagine. This fear must have been justified at a time when wages were so low that the temptation to supplement them in another way was too strong to be resisted. A note by Wilson Fox in the 1893 Report already quoted throws light on this:

'Bees and fowls are kept by some labourers, but not very generally. The keeping of pigs is rather the exception. In villages it is often impossible to do so on account of lack of garden accommodation, but where there are facilities fewer pigs are kept than might be expected. In this respect the Norfolk labourers are very different to those in the north of England, who almost invariably keep them, and it is the exception there to go into a cottage without seeing hams and bacon hanging from the beams in the ceiling. Some farmers in Norfolk stipulate that their men shall not keep pigs, on account of the temptation to take the farmers' meal home for their own animals.'

And again from the same Report: 'The question of manure

is a difficulty. It is the rule on most estates [in Norfolk] that cottagers must not keep pigs, because it is a temptation to them to take corn, etc.; and manure is too valuable a commodity for farmers to be able to afford to part with; whereas without it, of course, allotments are valueless.'

After the threshing the workers had to *dress* or winnow the corn, to clear away the chaff, the dust and the pieces of straw that were mixed with the grain. One method they had of doing this was to pin back the big double-door of the middlestead, also the smaller door on the opposite side of the threshing floor, and then to cast the corn into the draught that was set up. They had a special wooden shovel for this—wooden because it was less likely to injure the grain. It was called a casting shovel; in Suffolk it was called a *scuppit*, or *scuppat*, another medieval word that has survived in the dialect. In the nineteenth century a machine for winnowing became common. One machine which is still to be found in the corners of East Anglian barns and sheds is called a *blower*. It was an arrangement of five fans fixed to a central spindle that was turned by a crank. One operator turned the crank, while another fed the corn into the hopper. A third carried away the dressed grain. The blower was placed with its tail to the barn-door so that the wind helped to blow away the chaff. It was fitted with riddles of varying size of mesh, according to whether wheat, barley or oats was being dressed.

21. Bushel and strike

There were also wooden sieves in the middlestead to sift out dust and small seeds from the grain. The meshes were of thin cane or iron-wire. Other tools which have survived from this important process of dressing the corn are: the short handled-wooden hoe for filling the corn into the *maunds* or wooden containers for taking it up from the floor; also the *bushel*, the standard measure, a circular wooden drum with metal bands and two iron handles. With the bushel went a stick or *strike* for levelling off the top of the corn when the bushel had been filled. Both workers and farmers were very particular when filling corn into the bushel: if by chance the wooden scuppit or the scoop happened to touch the measure, thus jarring it and causing the grain to settle down, it was emptied immediately because in that state it would have more than its proper amount of grain. So careful, too, were they about the exactness of the measure of corn that the strike was drawn across the top of the bushel in a special way to prevent the grain from being pressed down. It was drawn straight across for wheat—a heavy grain—but for most other corn it was drawn across in a zig-zag fashion which apparently caused the least down-pressure on the grain.

22.
Barley-hummeller
or -awner

In the dressing of barley a special tool called a barley *hum-meller* or *awner* was used. This is a kind of iron grid with a handle about as long as a brush-handle. The iron grid was beaten lightly down on to the barley grain to remove the awns or beards.

Once again two verses from Tusser show how the process of *fyeing* the corn had not changed for centuries. (The word *fye* meaning to clean or dress was also used frequently by the old farm-workers here in connection with draining. I have often heard them speak of *bottomfying* ditches—cleaning out the bottom with a tool made for the purpose):

> *Once harvest dispatched get wenches and boys,*
> *and into the barn afore other toies;*
> *Choiced seed to be picked and trimly well fy'd,*
> *for seed may no longer from threshing abide.*
>
> *Get seed afore hand in a readiness had,*
> *or better provide if thine own be too bad:*
> *Be careful of seed or else such as ye sow*
> *be suer at harvest to reap or to mow.*

As Tusser advised, immediately after the corn was dressed seed had to be chosen. Up to recent years seed was also exchanged among farmers and gardeners. The old pre-machine-age farmer believed that if one grew a strain of seed on the same type of land for two or three consecutive years the yield would diminish. To remedy this a light land farmer or gardener exchanged his seed with another who farmed on the heavy land.

SOURCES AND BOOKS FOR FURTHER READING

A. WILSON FOX. *The Agricultural Labourer*
THOMAS TUSSER. *His Farming in East Anglia*
JOHN GLYDE. *Suffolk in the XIX Century*. Ipswich, 1856
C. HENRY WARREN. *Essex*. Robert Hale, 1950

9

Sheep and Cattle

Why have we given so much emphasis in the last few chapters to the growing and harvesting of corn? The answer briefly is this: East Anglia over a long period has had a very high reputation for its advanced methods of farming, and the region has won this reputation chiefly on its ability to grow corn. One of the reasons for this is East Anglia's nearness to the Continent. Most of the new techniques of farming came from the mainland of Europe down the years, and this region was on the front doorstep to receive and try them out. Thomas Fuller, the seventeenth-century writer, stated that gardening began to creep out of Holland into England during the reign of Henry VII; and along the Suffolk coast vegetables—notably carrots and turnips—were grown in gardens at this time: later they were sown in the field and became the key-crops in the arable farming of the region. Sir Richard Weston, the Royalist, who was an exile in Flanders and Brabant during the Commonwealth, brought back with him to England many farming methods he had observed over there. Most important of these was the growing of turnips in the field with the purpose of improving 'barren and heathy' land for corn crops—a technique on which the Norfolk improvers, Coke and Townshend, founded their new husbandry in the next century.

But there was a close link with the Continent from early times: East Anglia has always been exposed to military

93

invasion but it has likewise been in the path of new ideas. There is evidence that corn growing reached a high state of development even before the coming of the Romans and that corn was sent out of eastern Britain—but whether as tribute or surplus to the region's needs is uncertain. For corn is the natural crop of East Anglia because physical conditions here are perhaps better for its growing and harvesting than any other part of Britain. It lies on the dry side of Britain, on the lee side of the prevailing south-westerlies which cross the Atlantic and bring so much rain to the western side of the islands. The hard

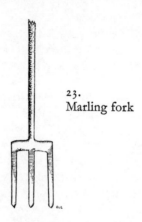

23.
Marling fork

winter frosts and the dry summers are ideal for preparing the seed-bed and ripening and harvesting the crop. The soil, too, with its large areas of boulder clay and drift material formed as a result of ice-action, is very suitable for corn growing; and even in the sandy coastal areas the chalky clay sub-soil is rarely too far from the surface to be tapped and spread on the land as marl.

Corn, then, is the farming crop best suited to the region. But that is not to say that it has been the chief crop throughout its history. For nearly a thousand years after the departure of the Romans farming was chiefly for use and not for the sale of its products on the market, and this meant that the traditional corn growing was mixed with the rearing of cattle, sheep and pigs. But during the fifteenth century, as already stated, the rearing of sheep for their wool was the first big deviation from the central line of corn growing in East Anglia. At this time the wool was sold abroad to the cloth-makers of northern Europe and Italy. Fortunes were made by the wool-growers or graziers. Vast quantities of wool went out from the region and from other parts of England, especially the Cotswolds. The wool was collected after the *clip* or shearing, made up into packs and sent on long trains of horses to southern ports like Dover and Southampton. From there much of the wool went to Calais which at that time was an English port. This chapter in East Anglian farming is brought to mind by the names which still survive in certain Suffolk villages along the routes which the pack-horses travelled on their way to the channel ports. *Calais* and *Callis Street* in the villages of Hadleigh and Boxford are two examples. The names of many inns along these routes are also a reminder of this former traffic: names like *Woolpack, The Fleece, The Golden Fleece, The Packhorse,* and *The Pack Saddle*.

The sheep-graziers of East Anglia were the fore-runners of the modern farmers. They were the first large-scale, capitalist farmers producing their crop—wool—as a commodity, not primarily for their own use or their neighbour's but for sale on a market that extended to the Continent and to the Mediterranean. One such grazier was Bassingbourn Gawdy who lived at Crowes Hall or Crows Hall near Debenham in Suffolk. He was a friend of the famous Springs of Lavenham who helped to give substance to the saying that many Suffolk churches were built on wool. Gawdy had ten flocks of sheep grazing at various places in Norfolk and Suffolk. Each flock was made up of between 450 and 700 sheep. *Flock IX* at Crowes Hall comprised 568 sheep, 'drafted thither from other flocks'. The big, red-bricked Tudor barns, used by Gawdy for storing his wool, are still in good condition at his home. A sheep's head is appropriately moulded in brick on one of its walls.

By the sixteenth century an embargo had been placed on the export of wool in order to assist the making of cloth in England. The East Anglian clothiers helped to make English cloth famous, and the success of the cloth-trade was another incentive to change farming from arable to pasture because there was much money to be made from the grazing of sheep. This change has been called the first great farming revolution; and indeed it altered the whole trend of husbandry and at the same time greatly affected society, causing much unemployment and social unrest. Sir Thomas More in *Utopia* made a devastating criticism of the new agriculture:

'There is an other [cause of stealing], whych, as I suppose, is proper and peculiar to your Englishmen alone . . . your shepe that were wont to be so meke and tame, and so smal eaters, now, as I heare saye, be become so great devowerers and so wylde, that they eate up, and swallow downe the very men them selfes. They consume, destroye, and devoure whole fields, howses, and cities . . . noblemen and gentlemen, yea, and certeyne Abbottes; leave no ground for tillage, thei inclose al into pastures; thei throw doune houses; they pluck downe townes, and leave nothinge standynge, but only the churche to be made a shepehowse. . . .'

If one may continue Sir Thomas More's metaphor, it would not be too much to say that the sheep first nibbled away the foundations of the open-field agrarian system and the medieval society that was its natural setting. Tusser's *farming in severalty* began in East Anglia to displace the open-field; and Tusser used up a lot of ink praising the new farming and pointing out the disadvantages that the old *champion* farmers laboured under. We are reminded of the period when sheep were in the ascendant by the number of surnames which derive from the occupations of this time and are still common in East Anglia: Weaver, Webster, Webber, Sherman or Sharman (Shearman), Dyer, Fuller, Card and Carder and so on. Occasionally, too, the name of a field or a part of a village has a link with the wool industry: for instance, *Copperas*, a field not very far from Blaxhall, was probably the site where copperas or copper sulphate was made for use in the dyeing of wool (it appears that this chemical was also used in tanning leather).

Undoubtedly there was a beneficial side-effect to the mass change-over from arable to grass. Indeed, some writers on farming history have put forward the theory that it was necessary to change from plough-land to pasture because, over the centuries, the soil was being progressively exhausted, and the declining yield of cereals compelled the change in order to allow the soil to recuperate. Others, however, have pointed out that in spite of the shrinkage in the total area of arable land during this period the resulting crops were adequate to feed a population that was actually increasing. But R. Trow-Smith in his *English Husbandry* has given figures of yields of wheat per acre to show that there had been an actual decline, and not all land was cropping efficiently. Sheep and enclosures, therefore, were not altogether the villains Sir Thomas More made them out to be.

But even after the English wool trade fell away, as it did in the seventeenth century, sheep-rearing remained still an important sector of arable farming in East Anglia, especially in the light, sandy lands of parts of Norfolk and Suffolk. Sheep *tathed* the land, to use a Norfolk word—fed the soil with their manure, urine, grease from their wool and even the warmth from their bodies when they were folded in pens on what later in the year became a seed-bed for the corn. It is certain that in the *sandlings* or sandlands of Suffolk, the sandy littoral, the old saying: 'The foot of the sheep turns sand into gold' was true to the letter. For in the time before artificial fertilizers it was only by a close tie-up between corn and sheep that crops could be grown with any success at all. In fact these light land areas became celebrated for the cultivation of barley. Under the Norfolk four-course system of rotating the crops, sheep were folded on the land after the harvest had been taken and winter-fed on turnips which became an essential root-crop in the rotation.

G

97

The Norfolk four-course or -shift was built on the principle that the farmer was never to take two corn crops in succession off one piece of land. With the use of turnips as a field-crop and by means of clover and artificial grasses he was able to carry out this rule fairly rigidly, interspersing either roots or grasses between his sowings of corn. By using the Norfolk rotation and having both a full fold of sheep and a full bullock-yard the farmer could be sure that he would then have a full granary. A farm contract (see Appendix One) shows that the four-course system lasted well into this century.

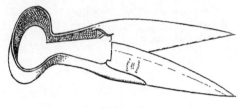

24. Sheep-shears

Many remnants of the old sheep farming are to be found in the villages of East Anglia. First is the sheep-shears, the tool used for clipping sheep. It is a very old implement; and it is certain that the Romans knew the principle of the sprung-handle shears. In the museum at Colchester there is an item from a Roman matron's toilet-set, a small pair of clippers only two or three inches long but identical in design with the sheep-shears. Modern flocks are of course sheared by machines; but in preparing sheep for display at agricultural shows the old shears are still used to make the final trimming of the fleece.

This is only an occasional use but it is surprising the number of shears still to be found in the countryside, all well adapted to secondary uses: hedge-clipping, trimming the edges of the lawn, thatching, and even the trimming up of graves. Yet none of these modern uses of the ancient implement is as surprising as one to which it was put when sheep-clipping was in its hey-day. I refer to its use for hair-cutting, a use that was once common in the sheep-rearing districts of England. It was so used by a part-time village barber in Blaxhall to 'take off the rough' before he used the scissors. One man in this village had one of his ears disfigured by a scar which lasted his lifetime. He got it when he was a lad through 'turning his head a bit sudden' when he sat in a chair behind the barber's cottage on Sunday morning over sixty years ago.

One can still see much of the shepherd's gear on the farm, tools that have not changed since the Middle Ages: the wheeled shepherd's hut, used at the lambing season, can still be found but probably converted into a chicken-shed. Sometimes, too, a shepherd will out of sentiment keep the small oil-stove he used in his hut for warmth or to heat milk to feed to an orphaned lamb: this stove was the successor to the medieval shepherd's charcoal brazier. An occasional shepherd has also kept his old horn lantern—lighted by a candle made from mutton fat, a complete survival from much earlier times. Robert Savage, the Blaxhall shepherd, used to swear by his old horn lantern and would use nothing else because, as he said, it gave out a gentle light which did not scare the ewes during the lambing season when he took it round the fold. The shepherd's crook is also kept but has become more of a museum-piece in some districts. This is very different from the fold-pritch, the heavy, pointed steel rod which the shepherd once used to drive holes for erecting his hurdles: the fold-pritch or shepherd's drove still does duty on the farm in a dozen various ways.

To return to our theme: The English wool trade declined during the seventeenth century, as already stated, and Charles II's attempt to help the clothiers and farmers by enacting that anyone who died should be buried in woollen cloth did very little to help the industry. The result was that the farmers, whose forebears had earlier gone over to grass, had now to change their methods drastically.

The great extension of London, the growing metropolis, at no great distance from their farms, was an opening for East

Anglian farmers. There they could sell not only their corn but butter, cheese and eggs, and also poultry. Robert Reyce, a seventeenth-century Suffolk historian, wrote that great attention was then being paid to dairy cattle in Suffolk: and their products found a ready market both at Stourbridge Fair—the famous Cambridge market dating from medieval times—and at London. Suffolk farmers also sold a great deal of their produce at this time to the growing Navy and to the increasing number of merchant ships that called both at London and the East Anglian ports. Suffolk butter and cheese became famous; but Reyce hints that it soon lost its reputation—'later this wonted estimation much abated'—because, owing to the demand, Suffolk farmers were tempted to increase the quantity of their dairy products at the expense of the quality. As Reyce neatly put it: 'Whilst the cheese was in the mak, the butter was at markett'; and he pointed the lesson that you cannot make good cheese after the cream had been taken off the milk to make butter. From this time Suffolk cheese gained a very bad name which followed it into the twentieth century.

But parts of East Anglia, especially the clays of central Suffolk, continued to specialize in dairy farming until the end of the eighteenth century. One witness to this is Arthur Young. He wrote about the dairy farming in High Suffolk, the district of heavy clays around Stradbrooke: although the farms here had been under grass for many years, during Young's time some of them were coming under the plough—but not for corn; they grew cabbages and roots to feed to milk cows and cattle. Also during the eighteenth century certain districts of East Anglia, chiefly the coastal marshes and the fens, fed the cattle that were driven down from Scotland to the Smithfield market of London to feed the capital's quickly growing population. This period of East Anglia's history is recalled by an occasional stretch of drovers' road in Norfolk and Suffolk that still survives as a grass-covered lane or track. As often, too, a field name is a reminder of the practice. While I was talking a few years ago to a Suffolk farmer, Charles Bugg (born

1883) of Barking, near Needham Market, he mentioned that a field near the church had the name of *Oxlands*. I assumed that the field was so called because, as in another parish I know, it was there that the last team of oxen in the district drew their final furrow. But the farmer told me this was not so: on this field the cattle, that used to be driven down from Norfolk in stages, stayed the night to rest. The next stage on their journey to Smithfield was the town of Sudbury, about fifteen miles away. These cattle had spent a season in Norfolk, fattening up after their long trek from Scotland.

The Napoleonic Wars caused high grain prices in Britain because little corn could be imported from the Continent to help feed the growing urban areas, and this induced East Anglian farmers to convert their pastures to tillage to grow more corn. But after the Wars, when grain prices fell sharply, farmers were compelled to adjust again. In fact, throughout the century the farmers of East Anglia had to devise means of meeting the challenge of the cheap corn that was coming into the country. This was especially so after the Repeal of the Corn Laws in 1846 took away the tariff barrier and left corn-growers more exposed to the world market. In fact, the whole of the nineteenth century is a demonstration of the lesson that farming had become as much welded into the country's economy as any industry, and was as much subject to the laws of commerce as it was to the laws—involving climate, soil and position—of natural growth.

The debate whether East Anglian farmers should specialize in corn-growing as the best type of farming for the region still goes on. And although it can be shown that the wetter, milder areas of the west are better placed for dairy farming (especially with the increasing speed and efficiency of transport of milk, for instance to the cities), yet natural advantages are not the whole story. Even with these in their favour, hard experience during the nineteenth century and later, has taught East Anglian farmers that the growing of corn as their main crop has sometimes left them in a very exposed position. But over the centuries it is chiefly in corn growing that they have pioneered new methods and new machines; and it is for corn growing that they have accumulated skills and techniques that have become almost instinctive. The present trend reflects this: about three-quarters of the land in the region is under the plough—the figure for Suffolk was 79 per cent in 1955. If I may judge from the trend in my own parish, where two farmers have sold their dairy herds in recent years, the percentage today is even higher than this.

The survivals of the old farming, the tools and the lore connected with it, also appear to show that corn growing has been the dominant interest down the years; and if farming has been forced to deviate from this central line at certain periods it always returns to it. There is also a great amount of lore connected with sheep; but, as we have seen, sheep and corn were tied together for centuries particularly on the lighter soils of East Anglia. Yet present-day farming in East Anglia is evidence that cattle have not been neglected: I refer to the Red-Poll breed of cattle which is native to the region and known widely outside it for its milking qualities. This breed of polled (hornless) cattle was evolved by Norfolk and Suffolk farmers during the seventeenth and eighteenth centuries when dairy farming in the region was in the ascendant. The breed was chiefly founded on the Scottish cattle which came south for the October and November fairs of Norfolk and Suffolk to be fattened for the London market.

But another connection with Scotland arose out of the great farming depression at the end of the last century. Some East Anglian farms, as Wilson Fox reported, were in danger of remaining uncultivated. Rather than let this happen landlords let their farms at extremely low rent. A number of Scottish farmers, attracted by these easy terms, which also included a waiving of crop restrictions, travelled south and took over these farms with very little capital. They very naturally farmed the land as they had done in Scotland; and they relied chiefly on dairy-farming, bringing Ayrshire cattle down with them.

Their methods met with much criticism from the East Anglian farmers who called the Scots 'land-skimmers'—that is, men who ruined arable land by over-cultivation and by not keeping religiously to the Norfolk four-course method of crop rotation. Yet the Scots were hard workers and they paid their way, chiefly by selling their milk in the London market; and they made a success of their farming at a time when many East Anglian farmers barely kept going, being in mortgage to the banks up to their doorstep.

Some of the relics of this period of dairy-farming and of the earlier ones are still to be seen in museums and private collections in the region. One of these is the milk-dish, used for holding the milk while the cream was separated from it. These are usually broad, shallow vessels made of wood and lined with metal (zinc or lead). Another type was the round wooden vessel, formed on the principle of a barrel with staves and metal hoops: it is about two feet in diameter and no more than four inches deep. The dairy maid took off the cream with a shallow metal utensil perforated with small holes. This was

25. Scotch cart with ladders fixed for carting hay, etc.

called a *fleeter* (*fleet*, meaning shallow, is often met with even today in Suffolk in connection with ploughing; but the name of this utensil derives from the Old English word *fleta* meaning cream). The broad and shallow milk-dishes also served as milk coolers.

At the end of the nineteenth century more complicated milk separators were invented. One of the simplest was a square, metal vessel which would hold four or five gallons of milk. It stood about eighteen inches from the floor, on four stocky legs. The dairy-maid poured the milk into the separator through a funnel at the side of the vessel. The funnel was connected with a pipe that ran outside the vessel to a shallow perforated well at the bottom. When the milk was poured into the funnel it gradually oozed up through the perforations at the bottom until the container was full. When the cream formed at the top it was conduited by a curved lip at the front to a tap at the side. A container placed under this tap collected the cream. Introducing more milk in this way through the bottom of the container had the advantage of not disturbing the cream that was forming at the top but of gradually easing it through the tap into the cream receptacle.

Butter-making, common on most farms in East Anglia, up to thirty years ago, has left behind many of its utensils: wooden butter *hands* for cutting up and weighing the butter, and attractively carved *stamps* or prints, for making a design on the weighed-out lump, were usually made of poplar wood which can be recognized by its shining whiteness when scrubbed. Occasionally one can find an old plunger-type butter-churn, but the hand butter-churns are fairly common and they still appear among the farm 'dead-stock' at the Michaelmas sales. In the Folk Museum at Cambridge there is a long rectangular wicker-basket, once used for carrying butter into Cambridge Market. Here butter was sold by the yard, as well as by weight. Selling butter by the yard probably grew out of the old University custom of allowing each college member who dined in Hall two inches of butter. This method of selling butter became illegal in 1922, a time when many medieval customs were being discarded.

A Helmingham farmer who recently turned out some attics in his farm discovered a set of cheese-vats. Like butter-making the making of cheese was a job in which each farmer's wife was expected to be expert. This cheese-making, too, is often brought to mind by the sight of a louvred window with wooden slats, instead of glass. It is usually at the back or the side of one of the timber-framed East Anglian farm-houses. Often the words CHEESE ROOM are carved or painted on a wooden plaque fixed above the window, indicating to everyone why the window was louvred.

An old stockman or shepherd will often keep some of the old tools of his craft. One of these is a *trochar* which an old shepherd once showed me. It is a device that was used by stockmen and shepherds to let out the gas from the stomach of an animal that had become *blown*. It was a kind of lance that incised the paunch in such a way that enabled the actual lance to be withdrawn, at the same time leaving a hollow tube in the incision. Through this the gas from the animal's stomach escaped. Another implement which once turned up in a Suffolk collection of old farm tools was also connected with first aid for cattle. This was a *probang*, a long leather rod that was introduced into the gullet of a beast that had swallowed an intractable piece of root—turnip, perhaps, or mangel-wurzel.

A *barnacle* or bullock-holder, sometimes called *dogs*, is also a relic of the time when dairy-farming in East Anglia was more widespread. It was used to clamp a beast by the nostril; and

26.
Barnacle
or dogs

it served the same use as the ring in a bull's nose, but with the difference that a barnacle could be removed quickly after use.

SOURCES AND BOOKS FOR FURTHER READING

C. S. ORWIN. *The History of English Farming*

The Agricultural History Review. Vol. V, Part 1, 1957

SUFFOLK RECORDS SOCIETY. *Suffolk Farming in the Nineteenth Century*

ROBERT REYCE. *Suffolk in the XVIIth Century* (1618). Edited with Notes by Lord Francis Hervey, Murray, 1902

M. BERESFORD. *The Lost Villages of England*. Lutterworth Press, 1954

W. G. HOSKINS. *Field Work in Local History*. Faber and Faber, 1967

ARTHUR YOUNG. *General View of the Agriculture of Suffolk General View of the Agriculture of Norfolk* ——(Third Edition, 1804)

R. TROW-SMITH. *English Husbandry*. Faber and Faber, 1951

LORD ERNLE. *English Farming Past and Present*

The Pattern Under the Plough. Faber and Faber, 1966

10

The Horse and the Horseman

In many ways the horse was the most important animal on the cornlands of East Anglia up to the Second World War. Power is essential for the proper cultivation of the land—ploughing, harrowing, sowing the seed, tending the seed-bed, and harvesting the crop—and the horse supplied it. The phrase *Good horses, good farm* summed up the need to have reliable power to make corn farming prosper. John Goddard, a Suffolk farmer who was born in 1855 and lived to see the modern farming revolution well under way, said just before his death in 1953: 'If poverty gets into the stable it will soon be all over the house'; and throughout his long farming life to breed good horses and to keep them in condition had been one of his chief concerns.

In Suffolk farmers changed over to horses from the medieval ox-teams very early compared with the rest of Britain. Records show that there were horse-teams working at the plough as early as the twelfth century. But at this early period horse-teams were very much fewer than teams of oxen and they remained fewer for a very long time because the heavy horse, the horse that is best suited to the plough, was too much in demand for battle. The heavily armoured knight needed the destrier or 'great horse' to enable him to take part in armed combat, the new kind of warfare which exploited the stirrup; and which the Normans brought to this country and used so effectively in winning it in 1066.

In the battle tactics as developed by the Normans on the Continent the war-horse and its rider acted as a kind of precursor of the modern tank. The horse was armour-plated at its front and it was schooled to plunge into the thick of the fighting, using its front hooves as weapons. But the most lethal weapon was the long lance which the rider, comparatively safe in the stirrups, held firmly under his arm for the charge. But gun-powder and the development of fire-arms changed all this. The medieval armed-combat type of warfare became outdated and the 'great horse', heavy enough to carry the tremendous weight of armour, was no longer needed. Lighter, more mobile horses were more suitable for the new type of warfare as the seventeenth-century Civil War in England soon showed.

The change in warfare roughly coincided with the break-up of the old medieval open-field system. In sixteenth-century Suffolk *champion*, as we have seen, was giving way to *severall*, open-field to individual farming; and for this the horse was the ideal animal, particularly the heavy horse which was now ready to serve the plough. It was faster than the ox and with the new, lighter ploughs that local enterprise was evolving, the horse became the motive power for agricultural improvement, and later on the essential means for the great farming revolution in eighteenth- and nineteenth-century East Anglia. There is some evidence to show that East Anglia had been known for the excellence of its horses from early times. Robert Reyce stressed the quality of Suffolk horses in the seventeenth century; and as the farming revolution developed, farmers began dimly to see the need to breed a horse specially for their purpose.

Arthur Young who became one of the leading spirits in this second great farming revolution urged Suffolk farmers to copy the example of Robert Bakewell, the famous Leicestershire stockbreeder and to improve their own native breed of horse—the ugly but strong Suffolk of the old breed—so as to make him the ideal animal for their farms. Later in the nineteenth century the farmers followed Young's advice and carefully bred the famous *Suffolk Punch*, a heavy chestnut developed specially for work on the land: sturdy in body, with short legs that made him an admirable animal for *drawing*, that is, for drawing a furrow with the plough. The Suffolk's great stamina and his particular shape or conformation of deep, well-rounded body (*a good bread basket*, as Suffolk horsemen said) enabled him to tackle the heavy clays and to work for a whole day's stint in the field without being fed, from the time of his 6 a.m. breakfast to his main meal between four and five in the afternoon.

A pair of Suffolks was responsible for ploughing about 50 acres of land during the year; and Suffolk farmers up to the coming of the tractor discussed the size of a farm in relation to the number of plough-teams it supported, in much the same way as the Domesday scribes characterized the farms in their survey of 1086. The phrase a *twelve-horse farm* told a Suffolk farmer or farm-worker the main points he needed to know about a holding: it would be about 250 acres in extent, probably a little more; it would have five regular plough-teams and perhaps a pair of older horses kept for *jobbing*, carting and doing some of the lighter work necessary on the farm.

The East Anglian horseman, who was also the ploughman—tending the horses as well as ploughing with them—took a great pride in his teams and in the standard of the work he did

27. Light farm trolley (Cambridgeshire)

with them in the field. We get the picture of his walking round the parish on a Sunday morning during the ploughing and drilling season, weighing up his own work against that of his neighbours.

George Sadler, the Cambridgeshire farmer, mentioned the care the horsemen took to keep their horses in condition:

'Look at the competition in those days. There'd perhaps be twenty stables of horses in one village. And they'd all be out to see whose horses would come out the best. Look at the pride they'd got in them. If you had horses yourself and somebody said to you:

' "Have you seen old So-and-So's horses? I've never seen horses like them in my life!" As soon as you went home that night you'd think to yourself: "Well, I'm a-going to beat him if I can," and you'd feed up your horses till they glowed.'

So intent was he on feeding his horses well and keeping them in a condition which the rest of the farms could look at with envy that he would try to scrounge extra rations for his horses from wherever he could:

'We used to roll oats for horses' food, my brother and me; and we used to pinch a sack or two of these oats and put it in the chaff. We used to dig a hole right down in the chaff-house and put a sack or two of these extra oats in there. Because we were allowed two hundredweight of oats a horse a week, and a hundredweight of maize when they were working hard. I used to go with my brother when he used to grind the oats and roll them out; and about this time I recollect we had a field of wheat and it looked a bit thin, not too heavy a crop. So we drilled some spring oats in it. Well, after that field was harvested we thrashed that corn out. Blast, it was some good grub. We used to soak it in an old tub. And the horses! well, after they'd been on that for a bit, their coats were just like raven feathers.'

George Sadler also told me how as a young lad working on his father's farm he used to help himself to the shepherd's food to feed to his horses, just to ensure they would look at least as well as anyone else's horses in the parish:

'Well, he didn't know I'd been pinching his corn till I got trapped. We used to keep some sheep; and next to my stable was the granary, with a slatted rail right to the top. It was locked and you just couldn't get through. We used to have those slabs of linseed cake in those days—the long slabs. And I got an old *muck-crone* [a fork with curved tines], and I used to put this muck-crone under the door and draw a slab of linseed cake through. Then I'd break it up with a hammer or a plough-share and keep it to one side; then I'd give it to the horses early in the morning before anyone got about. They'd eat that first and nobody would know. There's nothing like linseed cake for putting a gloss on their coats.

'Well, I used to get this linseed cake regularly until my father found me out. Then I started on the old shepherd's grub. He had a lot of locust beans in his lambs' grub, so I thought I'd have some of these. I started pinching the locusts, and the old shepherd—poor old boy, Old Tinny we used to call him—he twigged it, and he said:

' "I'm losing some of my sheep's grub, and I don't know where that's a-going."

'My father said to me: "Have you been taking that sheep's food?"

' "No, of course I haven't. What would I want to take that for?"

'I was about eighteen then, and my team of horses stood on one side of the stable and four other horses on the other. I'd been throwing some of this sheep's food up into the manger for my team: it was mostly split beans and locusts. And these damned old horses had got dainty and wouldn't eat the locusts. So when my father went up to the manger where my team was he put his hand along it, and there were the locust beans. That finished that lot!

'But I wasn't satisfied even then. One of my brothers used to look after cattle; and of course he had all the grub he could get hold of. And I used to go and start pinching the grub out of his tubs to feed to my team of horses. Of course he'd never

go down to the *net'us* [neat- or cattle-house] until about seven
o'clock to feed these bullocks he was looking after. But to feed
my horses before turning out I had to get up at four. Well, I
started pinching this cattle-food, and he soon guessed what was
going on, and he put a bloody rat-trap in one of his big barrels.
And the next time I went to scrape out a pailful of this
bullock's grub I got my hand in this trap.

'We were having tea that night and my brother said:

' "I got a rat in a trap in one of my tubs, but the darned thing
got away. I didn't get it." Then he looked at me: "But I
believe it was a two-legged rat that had been there. Let me have
a look at your fingers."

'He knew all right. But even after that I went on pinching
food for my horses. I really couldn't help it.'

Harold Smart (born 1889) who spent his working life with
horses in the Hargrave district of West Suffolk told me how
he kept his horses in condition with various herbs:

'We had all Suffolks at that time, and we looked after them
well and thought the world of them. We worked day and night
looking after them. We did everything we could so they could
work, and we rarely got any trouble. I doctored a lot of them
myself. I used bearsfoot, saffen [Tusser's *savin*], garden-tansy,
ferns from out of the bank. Bearsfoot was for condition, and to
keep their coats looking well. Saffen was a wonderful herb for
the coats, too. We used to use it on a Sunday morning: that
was the time when the horses kept the blood at the same pitch,
and the herb answered then. We grew the saffen ourselves,
and it was wonderful stuff for plumage, for coats. I've sold it
to a gamekeeper to mix with the pheasants' water—they used
it when they were a-rearing the birds to bring the plumage up
quick.

'I gave saffen to my horses in two ways. I boiled it in an old
pot, then I strained the liquid and then sprinkled it on their
food, each horse getting the right amount. I also baked it, dried
it, and made a powder of it. At that time o' day you could buy
hoss-powders from any chemist but we had to make our own.'

8. THRESHING DRUM, PORTABLE ENGINE AND TACKLE. Marlesford Hall Farm, 1910

9. RETURNING FROM THE FIELD (SUFFOLK). Cattle grazing roadside verge

10. TUMBRIL WITH FILL-HORSE AND TRACE-HORSE. Pond Hall, Ipswich, *c.* 1915

11. THRESHING WITH TRACTOR AND DRUM. Note rubber tyres on tumbril: a transition stage to full mechanization

This herb saffen was called the *threepenny bit herb* by some horsemen because the dosage for a horse was the amount that would cover a silver threepenny piece. It was highly dangerous to use and it was in fact poisonous if given carelessly. Some horsemen maintain that it has contraceptive qualities and if a mare was given saffen she would never get in foal.

Harold Smart also used ordinary epsom salts and bricklayer's lime. This was his best remedy.

'As for grease. When we had shire-bred horses we had a lot of grease—greasy legs. But I could dry that up and I could defy any veterinary to spot it. I've done it, and he's passed the horse as sound. It was all right if you started when the horse was young. I used white vitriol so it never showed. You had no grease, of course, with Suffolks. The most trouble we had with Suffolks on road-work was *splinters* and *side-bone*. If you got a horse with a side-bone [ossification of a cartilage in the lower leg] and you used it on the road, ten to one you'd get a splinter. Suffolks were subject to ring-bone on the shoulders occasionally, just where the collar went on, and then they became *collar-proud*—didn't like to have the collar put on them.

'I used the oils, the drawing oils for getting horses to come to you and follow you. Linseed oil was the first, and then we used to use oil of rhodium. We used to mix that with aniseed. That's what that old chap used to have with him when he pulled the hosses' tails. I'll tell you about that. He lived not far from here. His name was Turner, and he stole horse-hair from the tails. He'd have this drawing oil about him and he'd walk round the horses and get right for the wind; and the horses would come to him. Then he'd pull their tails to get the hair. He'd have a short piece of stick and twist it round some hair and chuck it out. He'd strip the tails, you know. But they caught him and he did jail for it. This was about 1897. I remember him well. He sold the hair of course. They used it for stuffing cushions and chairs and so on. There was a factory over here at Lavenham.

'The old chaps who came round with rags and bones would

buy up hair. They used to come to my stable; any old higgler would come and ask you if you'd got any horse hair. I sold plenty which I got through combing the manes and the tails. It was worth keeping because they used to pay 1s 8d a pound for it; and even if you'd got only a pound, 1s 8d was within threepence of the amount you got for a day's work.

'For a hard mouth in a horse we used oil of vitriol. That would give a horse a good mouth so you could pull him with a piece of cotton. We were forced to do it, because some were so hard-mouthed you couldn't do anything with them. There were some old men would put a clay-pipe stalk in the fire and when it was hot they'd put it on the side of the horse's mouth. It was a very cruel thing, you know, but they were forced to do it if they had a vicious horse that they couldn't work.'

George Sadler, who came from a long line of Suffolk horsemen, also recalled some of the herbs and cures his family had used:

'My old grandfather was always messing about with all sorts of cures. Penicillin wasn't a new thing to him: he used to make his own; and this was long before penicillin was heard of. He lived in a little thatched cottage, and he used to cut apples up into slices and put them in an old spare bedroom up under the thatch until they went mouldy. He gave the mouldy apple to a horse when he had a bit of a cold or was off colour, and he reckoned that would cure him. We couldn't go and buy anything in those days. There wasn't the money about. It didn't cost us anything to worm our horses, for instance; we wormed them with herbs. I know of some herbs—my father told me about them—that would cure a horse with a pricked foot quicker than any vet would; and it wouldn't cost you anything at all. This was marsh-mallows; and the one for worms was walnut leaves—I'm giving my secrets away now!— you dried the leaves up and gave them in the bait. Another thing we used for worming was horse-hair—some good strong horse hair, cut into lengths of about a half-inch each and put in with the food.'

As well as being very particular about the horses' condition the old horsemen were equally concerned about their appearance. Their coats had to shine like satin, and their harness had to be in as good condition as possible. They also had to be decorated with braid and ribbons even when they went out ploughing in the winter; George Sadler told me:

'We had to get into the stable very early in the morning to feed and braid up the horses. It took an hour and a half to braid properly. You always had to do the tails up summer-fashion or winter-fashion. There was never a horse went out unless that tail was done up. It had to be left long with just a little braid on the top and twisted underneath with a little bit of straw through for the summer. And the whole lot would be done up from the bottom as a winter 'do-up' to stop the mud from getting on to it.'

William Spalding (born 1896), who is still leading a thoroughbred stallion, has this to say about plaiting or braiding:

'As regards this plaiting business you've got to have bass, and you have six plaits running along to bring the bass on top of your hair which is a very difficult job to do. There are two different ways in plaiting horses' manes today and setting the ribbon up straight with the bows in the right position, and there are different ways in plaiting the tail. There is the *show* way to do him, and there is the *Michaelmas* way. I've plaited up hundreds of horses in this way when they were being sold at the Michaelmas sales. We used rye-straw then, not bass as we did for the shows; and we put a fan up on the tail, and finished up with a fan. And there is one way to plait these, to braid the hair up with the thumbs. But some people today have got the wrong idea: they braid down, and the plaits have gone inside; and the reason for this is that they've never learnt the right way.'

An unusual phrase often heard in connection with horses and the old corn harvest in East Anglia is *hoss howd yer*. John Withers, an Edingthorpe (Norfolk) farmer, has explained what it means: it was one of the first jobs a boy did in the harvest field. He led the horses as the harvest wagon was loaded up with corn, shouting to warn the men on top to hold tight as he moved on or bumped across a furrow:

'I remember when I went to school there were twenty or more horses on the farm; and you'd hear them every night and morning come along the road—loose. I remember seeing a man who'd usually ride one in front; and another man would ride a horse at the back. You'd hear them clumping along the road; full gallop they would come every night and morning when they had done harvest. The harvest was done on piece-work, and they were rattling up and down the road, full trot they would be, because the sooner they'd get it done the better it would be for them. And the boys would all be riding the front horses on the wagon, and shouting "Howd yer!" for the loudest. "Hold yer!" which means, Hold tight. I believe they paid the boys so much a harvest for doing that work. The reason they shouted that was that some men were on top of the wagon loading the corn, taking the sheafs that were pitched up from the ground by the others. The boys shouted "Howd yer!" and they would hold tight, knowing that the horses were about to move. And the boys only had to say this for the horses to start to move; for "Howd yer!" then was as good as saying to the horses, "Come along".'

Although, as we have stated, steam-power was used on the farms of East Anglia nearly a hundred years ago it did not make much impact on the organization of farming. The steam tackle was not suitable for all types of land; and some farmers found it expensive. John Goddard, the Tunstall farmer, bought a steam engine and plough-set made by Garrett of Leiston. It was called the *Suffolk Punch* and was designed to plough six furrows. John Goddard bought it for £700, but he found it too expensive to work: he ploughed twenty acres with it and scrapped it. He then returned to horses. It would be true to say, then, that horses supplied nearly all the power on the farms of East Anglia until the coming of the motor tractor just before the First World War. Therefore, keeping up the

28. Horse-hoe

stock of horses, good breeding was of first importance. George Sadler talked about this when we discussed the period of the First World War when he was a lad on his father's farm at Whittlesford. As the war went on the demand for heavy horses to pull the gun-limbers and for ordinary transport on the Western Front increased dramatically; for horses were being killed almost as quickly as men. And by 1917 the shortage of horses got so acute that the military authorities began to commandeer horses in this country wherever they could find them. An Ipswich man, H. E. Wilton, recalls seeing a horse on an Ipswich street being taken out of its cart by a party of soldiers: the cart was left on the side of the road for the owner to get home as best he could.

'During the First World War we hadn't any hay. All that went to France. It was all baled up, the thatch and the stack-bottoms as well. And we'd not got the horses then, because they used to come around the farms and commandeer all the best ones. We had some lovely horses. I remember one; I forget what we called him. But he was a good 'un. We went and hid him a long way away; but they found him; and they took him and some others—all into the Army. And, of course, we were left with only young horses to do the work. I know then we were breaking them at two year old and working them as if they were four year olds. All the horses, the five or six year olds, the hard, well-seasoned good horses, they'd all gone away to France.

'They went on the big artillery. And we had them back again, those that had been shell-shocked, frightened to death. (Of course, we'd always got our brood mares; they let us keep them because that was the only way of getting more horses. I think the Ministry, as far as I can remember, made it better for the small farmers to breed more horses then. They gave them assisted *nominations* to encourage horse-breeding because the horses were being killed faster than they were breeding; and it took three years to get a horse fit for anything.) Anyhow, I had one come back from France; he'd been shell-shocked. Oh, didn't I have a job with him! If he saw a soldier he'd go mad. I were only a boy, not more'n about sixteen, and I had a time with him. If he heard the report of a gun we used to have to go and put him in the stable, in the dark to let him settle down—poor thing.'

On one occasion during the First World War, just after they had lost some of their horses to the Army, George Sadler read in a newspaper that a transport ship carrying horses to France had been torpedoed in the Channel. 'I sat down and nearly cried thinking that one of our horses were in that ship when it went down. We had to breed, start breeding from two-year-old fillies to get foals as quick as we could to replace these horses. It takes eleven months to get one, and then it's running behind the mother. I remember we had five or six mares in foal every year. And when the time come for these mares to foal I used to go and stop up, sleep in the hay-rack with my father—to be with those mares. Because you're very lucky if you see a mare foal, you know. They'll deceive you. They're the quickest thing in the world: a mare can't stand a lot of pain; and I think they're a bit shy—shy about it, because they'll put it off if they can. We've had them and left them for a few minutes, and then gone back and found the foal—perhaps all right, or perhaps the foal has been suffocated. This is after you've been sitting up for a fortnight with her!

'But I recollect when my father used to be in the church choir; he'd sing in the choir. He could sing, too—well, he'd make a lot of row in any case! He used to say to me on a Sunday night: "Keep your eye on them two mares; they might foal before I get back again." He'd say:

' "If one of them looks like foaling, and sweats a bit, come and knock the little door at the side of the church."

'Oh, I used to keep running across the yard and looking at these mares, frightened to death one of them was going to sweat a bit. Anyway, one particular night, one of the mares did foal. But we'd only got an old lantern in this loose box—she were a big black mare, called Negress—she foaled and we hadn't got any paraffin to put in the lantern. The light went out; and he sent me round to the shop about eleven o'clock at night to get a pint of paraffin to put in this old lamp because we couldn't see what we were up to. And this mare wouldn't take the foal. She wouldn't take it at any price. The foal kept going to her and she kept kicking at it all the while. I think I sit and cried because she wouldn't take it.

'In those days we used to have stallions come round and cover these mares: they'd be travelling stallions. We used to get these mares covered at eight or nine days after foaling. That's the surest way of stopping a mare. And it was most important then: you wouldn't miss a mare if you could help it. It was a crime to miss a mare in those days; and if we got the mare covered at nine days we'd more or less think they were in foal again.

'Well, we used to wean these foals just before harvest-time; and of course the mares all had to go to work then to cart the corn. We didn't have no tractors, so the foals would be weaned, and the mares would be at work again; and a rare job we used to have with some of the mares. Perhaps a mare had been away from the foal for three days and you daren't leave them. You had to draw the drop of milk out of them, ease the bags off at night. It was a job; but, there, it was all in the day's work. We had to do it and we did do it. I used to have to stand and hold these mares under the stacks, frightened they'd keep calling out to these foals, and they'd slip off and throw somebody off the wagon or something. If we got a bad 'un she always went on the horse-rake.'

Breeding and sex in general were a part of the natural order of things to the people of the old farming community; and this is another aspect of it that reminds us of its ancient roots. It is exactly the same attitude as we find in Chaucer's *Canterbury Tales*; and it is no exaggeration to say that a Suffolk stallion leader, like Charles Rookyard, was in direct line with the carter in the *Friar's Tale*. Like him he called one of his horses *Scot*: like him, too:

> *This carter thakketh (pats) his horse upon the croupe (rump)*
> *And they begonne drawen and to-stoupe*

in exactly the same way as the Suffolk Punch would get down or stoop on to its knees in its efforts to draw a full or heavy load. And his attitude to breeding and increase was as matter-of-fact as that of some of the pilgrims who went to Canterbury in the fourteenth century. This comes out in Charles Rook-yard's (1889–1965) description of an incident when he was leading his stallion, *Sudbourne Benedict*, around some of the farms in the Helmingham district:

'I once met a parson when I was travelling with an entire horse, and he said:

' "Hullo! Good morning, young fellow."

'I said: "Good morning, sir."

' "I would love," he said, "to go along with you just to see this horse do the work."

' "Well," I said, "there's nothing to stop you. I'm now a-going to Mr Gooding's, straight to his farm, Redhouse, Witnesham.

You can come if you like. There's nothing wrong about that."

' "Well," he said, "I would like to come. Do you drink beer?" I said: "That I do. That's just one of my main points."

' "All right," he said, "I'll go and get a bottle," and he went and got a bottle of ale and brought one out for hisself. I thought to myself, "You got good religion in you, and this is better than drinking tea."

'So he brought my bottle out and poured his out and we tapped glasses together. He says:

' "Here's good luck."

'I said: "Thank you very much, sir."

'And he said: "I'll come on with you."

'So he came up to the farm, and they had a job for my horse, which he was very interested in. And when I started back, he said:

' "Are you coming back past mine?"

'I said: "Yes, sir."

' "Well, we'll have another drink. Can you drink another?"

' "Sure," I said, "that would be just my hobby."

'He said he never was so surprised in his life. He never thought anything like that would happen.

' "Yes, sir," I said. "That's nature with a horse, just the same as there's nature with the human beings."

'And what his idea was, in a way I suppose, was just to see the position which I had to get the horse into before he had the job with the mare; and he wondered how the job was done with the harness I'd got on. But I used to take all the harness off, hold the horse back, and I said, "Right!" and the job was done.'

There we have in one of its aspects the likeness of the old country society that has just passed away to the society described by Chaucer: a cool, matter-of-fact treatment of a subject that could have so many overtones. To Chaucer, as to the old countryman, what we might regard as broad or even bawdy is a plain fact of nature, as neutral or objective as—to use Chaucer's own word—the engendring of the simple flower.

SOURCES AND BOOKS FOR FURTHER READING

Suffolk Horse Society Stud Book. Vol. I, Edited by Herman Biddell. Cupiss, Diss, Norfolk, 1880

ANTHONY DENT AND DAPHNE GOODALL. *The Foals of Epona*. Galley Press, 1962

WRIGHT, C. *Farm Horses*. Young Farmers' Club Booklet. Evans Brothers, 1951

BRIAN VESEY-FITZGERALD. *The Book of the Horse*. Nicholson and Watson, 1946

GEOFFREY CHAUCER. *The Canterbury Tales*. World's Classics Edition, Oxford University Press

The Horse in the Furrow

11

The Harness-maker

The horseman took a great pride in his horses, as we have seen; and when he turned out on the highway he was careful to see they were braided up, the brasses highly polished, and the *bounces*—the 'lovely coloured worsted', as one horseman called them—properly displayed. Many Suffolk horsemen, when occasionally they took their horses to Ipswich market, rose very early in the morning—3 o'clock, or even earlier—to put the finishing touches to harness they had perhaps oiled the night before, and to paint the horses' hoofs with harness oil to make them look smart. The horseman was very particular about his harness and was as much concerned as the farmer to keep it in good order, making frequent visits to the saddler or harness-maker who had his shop in most of the larger villages.

Here is an account from one of them, Leonard Aldous (born 1900) of Debenham. He has been a harness-maker for most of his working life and he is still in business:

'I've just completed 51 years [1964] in the business. I left school at the early age of twelve and a half, my father having died when I was nine. We were living quite near a saddler's shop in Debenham, and I was always interested in it. The old gentleman who was the owner of the shop encouraged me and helped me along into the business. I went as an apprentice to him, starting on March 17th, 1913. My wages were sixpence

per week. If I'd been fourteen years old I should have com-
manded one shilling, but being only twelve and a half I got
sixpence.

'After I'd been at the shop roughly eighteen months—that
was in August, 1914—the Great War broke out; and as two of
our workmen joined the armed forces I had more or less to be
pushed on. Within two years of starting my apprenticeship I
was having to do roughly a man's work, but my wages were
only half-a-crown a week.

'We used to go round the farms to collect the harness-work
and bring back sets of harness for repair. But in my early days
it was quite common for some of the old horsemen to walk
anything up to two or three miles, and sometimes more, to
bring harness down to the shop. They came down in their own
time, after they'd left off work, and they'd have a small job
done; and then they'd take it back ready for work the next
morning. The main reason was that these horsemen were so
jealous, in a way, and particular about their horses that they
wouldn't put another piece of harness on belonging to another
horse. Each horse had his own harness; and if it couldn't be
spared to be sent down to the shop for repair, the horseman
brought it himself, got it seen to and took it back ready for
work on the next day.

'He made a special journey walking, as I say, perhaps three
or four miles. But I should say very often the old Guv'nor
would let him have either a shilling to go down to the pub
while we did the job, or else he would provide him with a jug
of home-brewed beer and bread and cheese. The Guv'nor
used to brew his own beer in those days as most people
did.'

But the harness-maker was directly involved with the farm
in another way, as Leonard Aldous recalled:

'We contributed to the harvest *horkey* or *largesse-spending*, the
frolic the men had after the harvest was gathered in. Usually the
horseman on the farm—the head horseman—came round after
the harvest and made a collection from the various tradesmen

who'd had business with the farm—saddler, farrier, wheel-wright and so on. When I was young the money the tradesmen gave went to augment the beer-money for the frolic. The farmer probably found the food and our largesse-money was used to find the beer. Very often, too, when we were travelling round the farms doing repairs (and many of these were done just before harvest to prevent hold-ups at a busy time) the Guv'nor would tell us to leave two shillings at a certain farm, half-a-crown perhaps at another, and at some only a shilling: that would go towards the men's largesse-spending.

'I well remember one of the first outside jobs I did as a lad. It was to repair, or help to repair, a set of leather bags for some bellows in a smithy about three miles away from our village. I had to go down there with the Guv'nor. I was rather intrigued when I heard about this job, being barely thirteen years old, wondering exactly what I had to do. Of course, one of the fellows at the shop took it upon himself to explain what my job was. We had to stitch a patch on one of the bellows. There was a little air-hole at the top of the bellows, called the *clack*, and my job was to crawl through that to the inside of the bellows; and I could then turn the needle as the Guv'nor stitched from outside! I had a surprise when I saw the bellows and I didn't know what to think about the job.' [But apprentices were fair game at that time of day: it was like sending you for a block of pigeon's milk or a couple of penn'orth of strap oil.]

When Leonard Aldous started in the harness-maker's shop the business was often referred to by a different name. A farmer might tell one of his workmen: 'You'd better take that *dutfin* [bridle] to the *knacker's*.' Both these words were used in medieval times; and we can understand the word *knacker* as an equivalent for harness-maker when we learn that it comes from an Icelandic root, *knakkr*, meaning a saddle. The old saddler used to prepare and tan the leather himself, and even slaughter the horses; and this last function has given the word its more usual modern meaning.

The Harness-maker

Leonard Aldous used the same tools and made the same type of harness as his predecessors did in medieval times. Some of them are described by Tusser in his *Husbandly Furniture*:

> *Whole bridle and saddle, whitleather and nall,*
> *with collar and harness for thiller and all.*

Whit- or white-leather was leather that had been dressed with alum, and it was often horse-leather. A nall is an awl (compare nadder, the original form of adder). Thiller—often *fill'us* or fill-horse in the East Anglian dialect—was a word Shakespeare used in *The Merchant of Venice*. It meant the horse that was placed between the shafts of a cart, as opposed to the trace-horse which pulled in front of the thiller.

The saddler also talked about the rope-walk that was once at the back of his shop. (This saddler's shop, with 'a rope-spinning ground' behind it was sold by auction in July 1875 at the Lion Inn, Debenham.) There they made rope for the plough-lines, the reins or *cords*, as the horsemen invariably called them. Hemp, from which the ropes were made, was grown in parts of East Anglia until this century; and an old countryman is often able to point out the site of an old *rett'n pit*. This was a pond in which the hemp was soaked or retted to loosen the rough fibres, the first stage in its preparation. Tusser mentions it (as he does most things connected with the East Anglian farm) under his *September Husbandry*:

> *Now pluck up thy hemp, and go beat out the seed,*
> *and afterward water it as ye see need;*
> *But not in the river where cattle should drink*
> *for poisoning them and the people with stink.*

A Suffolk man, Percy Wilson (born 1884) of Witnesham, has supplied a note about the saddler's business. His father was in the trade; and when he was a boy, he and his brother had a daily task as soon as school was over: 'We had to take the hemp and roll it up and treat it with beeswax. We described the threads as "four of the fine, two of the coarse and so on". We became expert as we'd done so much of it. We had to do it every night so it could be ready for my father's work next day.'

SOURCES AND BOOKS FOR FURTHER READING

The Horse in the Furrow (Chapter 16)
See also : Old Farm Sales Catalogues
Harness Makers' Catalogues

12

The Tailor

The farm horseman had almost as much regard for his own appearance as he had for that of his horses. He took a great pride in his clothes; and since he had a couple of shillings more a week than the ordinary day-labourer he was able to save a little and get himself a very good suit of clothes. How good his clothes were Sam Friend of Framsden, Suffolk, testifies:

'I was talking to a man in Cretingham Bell the other night [June 1964], and I was saying I'd got a coat, a brown melton, I had made for me in 1911. It's as good now as when I bought it. Anyone can come and look at it if they want to. And this man said to me:

' "I dussn't go to the tailor's now"; and I said:

' "For why not?"

' "It's too dear at the tailor's today," he said.

' "I don't see that," I says; "when wages were ten shillings a week that used to cost me five guineas for a suit of clothes. Now I had to work ten weeks to get that amount o' money. And it never paid for the suit even then. Now do you count up ten weeks of a farm-worker's wages today."

' "Well, I never thought of it that way," he said.'

A Debenham tailor, H. E. Rowe, confirmed that the farm horseman took a great interest in his clothes. He thought that this was partly due to the competition set up at one time by the big estates in the neighbourhood. In many of these, the estate

12. BELL FARM, FRAMSDEN (SUFFOLK) *c.* 1908. These 25 men cut 25 acres of barley before noon, after starting at 6 a.m. The farmer is holding a jar of harvest beer. Note barley-bale on scythe near centre

13. MARES AND FOALS. Bocking Hall, Helmingham (Suffolk)

14. DEBENHAM (SUFFOLK) *c.* 1917

15. EARLY CORN HARVESTING MACHINE. A Bamblett grass-cutter
adapted to cut corn. One man swept the corn off the platform with
the rake (left), another drove the horses

employees—the gamekeepers, gardeners, grooms and horse-men—used to be fitted out by the estate tailor with a good suit every year. The farm horseman, then, was determined to be on an equal footing with the estate horseman he met in the pub; and he got himself a good suit, probably from the same tailor. But the horseman was very conscious of his dress whether he was in competition with estate employees or not; and East Anglian horsemen often spent as much on a suit of clothes as the farmer—or even the squire. The Debenham tailor has corroborated Sam Friend's account:

'I recollect some of the old horsemen from this area—such as Sam Friend. Sam has been coming to our shop all his life, since he was a boy of fourteen; that is, in my grandfather's, my father's and in my time. He came here in 1910 or 1911 for a brown melton suit. But on one occasion, not very long ago, he wanted me to make him a pair of cord trousers. He said:

' "I don't know what the price is now, Mr Rowe. But in your grandfather's time the trousers would cost one week's wages—which was ten shillings. And for a brown melton suit it cost me ten and a half weeks' wages—which was five guineas. So at that rate, if I have the cord trousers it will cost me the present week's wages, which is £8."

'I pulled his leg a bit and I said to him:

' "Right. And if you want to repeat the order for the brown melton suit you had it will cost you ten and a half weeks' wages. And you'd be satisfied with £85?"

'Sam laughed; and I really believe that if he wanted another brown melton suit he'd have got it—even at that price! But I've heard my father talk about another family from Otley who used to come to the shop regularly years ago. One man in particular from this village of Otley used to wear very tight-legged trousers. He had them so tight he used to strap them up to a beam in his bedroom and drop himself into them and wriggle himself until his legs got right down. It must have been a proper business to get them off at night.'

When the farm-workers made one of their rare visits to the

town, usually after they had had their harvest wages, they did their buying for the year. Arthur Pluck (born 1888), a Stow-market clothier, described them coming to the shop in his father's time, between sixty and seventy years ago:

'These old country DO's would come into the shop to buy their ware, their outfit. And Father always kept underneath the counter in those days a four and a half gallon tub of beer (it was bought locally and was about three-farthings a pint); and before they started buying they'd say to one of us:

' "What about it?"

'We knew what they meant. That would mean a glass of beer before they started business. Well, when they'd finished that, they'd look around—time was no factor; they were in town for a bit of a spree as far as their money allowed them—and they'd say:

' "Well, might as well wet the other eye, Guv'nor."

'That meant, of course, they wanted another glass of beer before they started buying. Well, we gave them another glass; they finished it, and eventually they got down to business. Probably they wanted to buy a pair of cord trousers. But they would want to pay for these cord trousers before they bargained for another item. They wouldn't treally trust us to count up a lot of items. They couldn't count very well themselves, and they bought very cautiously. But they'd pay for the trousers and then they'd ask for a pair of hob-nail boots (my father used to keep boots as well in those days); we called them *deckers* and they used them for work on the land. They'd then buy a shirt, and pay for each garment individually right through the outfit. And he could buy the lot out of his gold sovereign and still have some change. But apart from the difference in money between then and today, look at the change in tempo. We couldn't waste time like that in these modern days.'

Arthur Pluck often used to go with his father into the country to sell clothes in the villages and to measure up the farm-workers for suits:

The Tailor

'But transport was bad in those days, and some of the farm-workers from the rather outlying districts couldn't get in to our harvest sales. So Father would go out to have a country sale, offering the goods at our harvest-sale price. He'd take out a ton and a quarter, or a ton and a half, of stuff by horse-transport; and we used to hire a club-room in a country pub where we could hold our sale.

'The old bo's would come in, and my father and I used to go down to the bar to *kick off with*. The men in the bar would look at us rather staringly; and one would get up with his pot of beer. It was an ordinary earthenware mug: you don't see it in the pubs nowadays unless it's hung up for ornament. And he'd offer you a drink out of his mug. It was rather unhygienic, but that was the custom in those days; and we had to do it because they'd think it was an insult if you didn't drink with them. But they were very artful. They used to leave a little at the bottom of the mug, and you'd have to pay to have it filled up again. But still, we didn't mind that. That was their way of life and their amusement; and we did business in their way.

'After we had our little bout in the tap-room they'd come in and buy what they wanted: cord trousers, hob-nail boots, shirts and so on. And they'd probably want a little bit of best wear: black jacket and waistcoat and a muffler, an art silk muffler. We used to have these mufflers in all colours of the rainbow. And they often bought the old *billy-cock* hat the horsemen used to wear. It was a black hat with a rather high, pointed crown; and it had a wide black band round it. I remember that a good billy-cock had oak-leaves worked on the black band; and they looked rather smart. They were a more or less soft hat. But they're gone out now. I don't think anyone in the trade at the present time would know what a *billy-cock* was.

'There was a big range of *cords*—corduroys—at that time. There were the plain cords and the variegated ones. There were many kinds of these—the pheasant-eye and so on, several kinds. But the one I remember best was a nine shaft, a plain cord. We used to sell a lot of it. I used to visualize it as I went round the countryside in the autumn when they ploughed. The design of the cord was exactly like that of a field when they used the horse-plough—with the stetches and their furrows out straight as a die for sowing.

'We also used to supply the old packmen who did business in the countryside. I remember one of them well, a Mr Ploughman. When he first started he sold packets of tea and odds and ends round the countryside; but after a time he used to come into the shop. He'd buy four or five pairs of braces and five or six pairs of socks. He'd take *orders* in the villages, and I've known him on many occasions pack up a pair of cord trousers that he'd got an order for. When he finished as a packman he gave me the old stick on which he carried his pack: I've got it here now under the counter.'

Arthur Pluck showed me the stick, an ordinary nut-wood or hazel stick which the packman had spotted in a hedge on one of his tramps around the villages and had chosen for the smooth bend that fitted his shoulder perfectly. As I looked at it, it struck me that this was the kind of stick the rural Autolycus carried around in Shakespeare's day, bringing his pack to the villagers who readily bought his ballads and his oddments and trinkets and eagerly lapped up his gossip and his tales that helped to lighten their country isolation.

There is another picture of the type of clothes the Suffolk horsemen wore seventy years ago. It comes from William Denny (1882–1968) of Ashbocking. He started work on a Suffolk farm, but his youth coincided with the bad depression already mentioned; and winter and early spring often found him—like many others—without employment. Dozens of young men left the Suffolk villages at this time as soon as harvest was over and they spent six months in the maltings of Bass, Ratcliffe and Gretton at Burton-on-Trent. They returned at the end of May, just in time for the *haysel*. But they invariably bought a new suit of clothes before returning to Suffolk. William Denny recalled:

The Tailor

'You dussn't come home from Burton wearing the suit you went up in. I used to buy my suit at a Burton shop called Tarver's. I believe it's still in the town. The suit had what we used to call a *donkey-dealer's* jacket. It was cut long, half-way down your thigh, and it buttoned up tight almost up to your neck. It had a long centre-vent at the back and a shaped waist with a couple o' buttons.'

This was essentially the same style of garment that Sam Friend had made for himself in 1911, a jacket which he occasionally refers to as his 'morning coat'.

SOURCES AND BOOKS FOR FURTHER READING

The Horse in the Furrow (Chapter 6)

13

The Blacksmith

The blacksmith and the wheelwright in most East Anglian villages had their shops next door to each other. The circular steel plate occasionally to be seen outside a smithy (there is one still in position outside Brandeston forge in Suffolk) is a reminder of this co-operation. This steel plate was the tyring platform: here the wheel that the wright had made was fixed while the smith and his men gave it an iron tyre. Both trades were closely linked to the farm, chiefly because the horses and wagons could not be kept in condition without the help of smith and wheelwright. Up to the beginning of this century most of the repairs to farm implements were done by these tradesmen. The blacksmith also made the tools, and the smith who could make a well-tempered hoe which had a thinner and lighter blade, which nevertheless lost nothing in strength, would command a custom that was much wider than his own village. For an ounce or two's saving in the weight of a hoe-blade meant a tremendous saving of energy to a man who wielded the hoe twelve or fourteen hours a day, hoeing sugar- or cattle-beet and—earlier during the last century—hoeing between the *ringes* or rows of corn. The same principle applied to the sickle and the scythe which a village smith often made specially for a particular worker's need. *Blacksmith made* in East Anglian villages, even today, is the highest praise one can give to a hand tool.

The Blacksmith

Some of them, as we have already noted, have not changed either in design or function since the beginning of the Christian era. Tusser in his list of *Husbandly Furniture* includes many such tools that were in general use until the 'twenties, and are still to be found in sheds or barns, and sometimes adapted to a secondary use on the modern farm or garden:

> *A pitch-fork, a dung-fork, sieve, skep, and a bin,*
> *a broom and a pail to put water therein;*
> *A hand-barrow, wheel-barrow, shovel and spade,*
> *a curry-comb, mane-comb, and whip for a jade.*

> *A grindstone, a whetstone, a hatchet and bill,*
> *with hammer and English-nail sorted with skill;*
> *A frower of iron, for cleaving of lath,*
> *with roll for a saw-pit, good husbandry hath.*

> *A short saw and long saw to cut a-two logs,*
> *an axe and an adze to make trough for thy hogs;*
> *A Dover Court beetle and wedges with steel,*
> *strong lever to raise up the block from the wheel*

A *frower, fro* or *froward* is still used for cutting lengths of wood for a beech fencing. A beetle is a heavy wooden mallet, made in Suffolk out of an *ellum tod*, a knotted piece of elm wood. But George Sturt distrusted elm for a beetle and preferred either beech or apple-wood. (Apple-wood was used for this in Saxon times. Beetley, the name of a Norfolk village, means 'the wood in which beetles or wooden mallets were got.' It appears that crab-apple trees were once common in this district.) The blacksmith bound the mallet with a steel band at each face to prevent it splitting when the steel wedges were driven into the logs. After constant use the wood on the edges of a beetle became frayed and curled over. This, a common image to the countryman, gave rise to the expression *beetle-browed* to describe a man with heavy, projecting brows. We know that the beetle is a much older implement than the Tusser reference would suggest, since the expression beetle-browed is found in Langland's *Piers Plowman*. Shakespeare also used the expression *beetle-headed* in his sense of stupid. Nails were often driven into the face of a beetle to prevent or at least lessen this fraying of the wood; and beetles so treated sometimes come to light in the country villages during the summer season when they are a useful tool for driving in tent pegs and posts for the various side-stalls at a country fête.

Tusser also mentions the *dung-crone*, the fork with bent tines or prongs made by the village smith. This implement is called a muck-crone today in East Anglia and is still in use, as George Sadler illustrated when he described filching the stockman's oil-cakes. Tusser also lists the smith's own tools and equipment:

> *A buttrice and pincers a hammer and nail,*
> *and apern and scissars for head and for tail.*

A buttrice is a tool for trimming the horse's hoofs—especially the *frog*, the horny pad at the centre of the hoof. It is no longer used because modern farriers recognize that it is wrong to cut the frog since it acts as a kind of shock-absorber when the horse places his hoof down on the road: also, through the pressure thus exerted on it, it assists the circulation of blood in the hoof. Instead of a buttress the present-day smith uses a knife. A blacksmith who is still shoeing horses told me: 'A

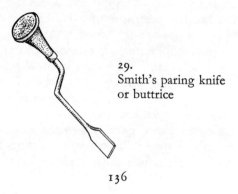

29.
Smith's paring knife
or buttrice

136

hammer, pair of nippers, a rasp and an unclencher—for taking off the old shoe—are all you want for shoeing.'

The *apern* that Tusser lists is the leather apron that most smiths still wear. Hector Moore, a Suffolk blacksmith, whose family has been smithing in the village of Brandeston for at least two centuries, wears a leather apron with frills cut into the bottom of it. Once he told me, with a twinkle in his eye, how the frills came to be there:

'The smith is the next best man to the Lord. For the Lord changed water into wine and the smith changed old iron into new; and if you ask a smith how he got the frills at the bottom of his leather apron he'll probably tell you something like this: The blacksmith was once considered the most important man next to the King. So when the King gave a feast to all his craftsmen he had the smith sitting next to him in the place of honour on his right hand. There was a little bit of jealousy among the other craftsmen because of this; and the tailor who was sitting opposite the smith particularly didn't like the favour shown to him. He said nothing, though, but while the feast was going on he quietly took out his scissors and slyly snipped the smith's leather apron under the cover of the table, putting his malice into every cut in the leather.

'Of course,' the blacksmith explained after he'd finished his story, 'you haven't got to believe a word of it! I myself cut the frills in the bottom of this leather apron I'm wearing; and I did this for a very good reason. Often when I'm hammering a piece of hot iron, the scales drop off on to the anvil and mess up the work. To get rid of 'em, I only have to lift up the edge of the apron, bunch it in one hand, and I've got a brush that'll sweep the anvil clean with one flick.'

The smith in his capacity of farrier, or shoer of horses, was also well recognized as an expert on their diseases; and he was of the greatest value to the farmer in looking after the feet which many breeders—especially of the heavy horse—considered to be the horse's most important part. Good feet were the first condition for a working horse; and some farmers

137

consulted the smith before buying a horse, asking him his advice about the feet which, from the nature of his job, he knew intimately. The blacksmith too—more than one smith has claimed—through attention to the horse's feet, correcting a fault, for instance, by making up a special shoe, has won many show prizes for farmers. He has made it possible for a horse to show convincing *action* in the show-ring, walking and trotting under the judges' eye, whereas without this attention the horse would scarcely have been taken to the show-ground.

The smithy was a natural place for men to congregate when the old farming economy was in its hey-day, before mechanization broke it up and did away with the farm-horse. Farmers and farm-workers bringing their horses to be shod waited round the forge or the *trav'us* while the horse was being attended to. (The *trav'us* is the stall adjoining the forge: here the actual shoeing took place. The word is probably *trave-house*. A trave is a wooden frame once used to confine a difficult horse or ox while it was being shod. Chaucer used the word in *The Canterbury Tales: She sprong as a colt doth in the trave*.) The bystanders were often joined by those individuals who find a fascination in watching other people work. But we must remember that this was a more leisurely age and it was understandable that the smithy became one of the gossip-shops in the village.

A Needham Market smith, Clifford Race (1898–1958), told me:

'There was plenty doing in the smithy when it was only horses on the farms. Sometimes there'd be eight or nine people standing about there swopping news—market news and just ordinary gossip. You hardly had room enough to do your job, but you daren't tell 'em to get out o' the way; or else they'd say they'd as much right to be there as you had! You had to go a-shoeing the horse as best you could. At election time it were well nigh impossible.'

But this reputation of the smithy was a very old one, as it appears that there was an ancient Nordic law which stated that a man was not to be held responsible for what he said at the forge.

The Blacksmith

But whenever a young colt was brought to the smithy for its first shoeing few people would be found to stand around. For a colt always objected violently to having an iron shoe nailed on to its hoofs; and sometimes the smith and his assistants were thrown about the trav'us as they tried to get the young animal under control. It was no place for idle talk then: there was too much action for gossip. The danger and the extra effort needed to shoe a colt for the first time was recognized by a custom called in some districts of East Anglia by the term *First Nail* which presumably referred to the violent shock the first nail would give to the colt. Under this custom the colt's owner paid a shilling over and above the actual cost of shoeing so that the men could send out for six pints of beer as a reward for the extra effort involved.

The custom also had its echoes on other occasions. A new apprentice to the smith was treated in a symbolic way like the young colt. The men in the smithy seized him; and one of them took a hammer and drove a nail into the sole of his boot. He stopped only when the boy shouted 'Beer!', thereby agreeing to buy his new work-mates a pint each of beer. In the Brandeston forge the smith kept a four and a half gallon barrel of beer under the bench, and the men got their allowances of *First Nail* from this.

There was also a custom by which a boy at his first harvest under the old system of farming went through the ordeal of *First Nail* or *Shoeing the Colt*. As soon as he entered the first field to be cut his mates up-ended him and gave him the same treatment which stopped only when he shouted 'Beer!'.

The skill of the East Anglian blacksmiths and their co-operation with the farmers is shown in the pioneering work of this region in the making of farm machinery. Two world-famous makers of farm machinery, Garrett of Leiston and Ransome, Sims and Jefferies of Ipswich, started in the early nineteenth century, as small businesses that had developed out of the village-smith scale. For years Ransome's of Ipswich employed smiths in their factories each with forge and anvil,

The Blacksmith

such as they had used in the village smithy before joining the big firm. Arthur W. Welton (born 1884) gave me an account of how he had moved from a village smithy at Benhall in Suffolk to Ransome's Ipswich factory:

'I was in the country blacksmith's for five years. Then I left and came to Ipswich and I was employed by Ransome's in the plough-shop. I went to the plough-shop in 1903 and that was barely finished. James Edward Ransome was so keen and pleased with the shop being such a big size he had a engine go over the floor to test it. It proved satisfactory and when I first went to the shop in that year I was trying to look through it, wondering when I'd get to the end. It was so wide and long. I had a forge of my own just as in the Benhall smithy. During my time at the forge in Ransome's plough-shop my job was making parts and assembling ploughs for this country and almost every country in the world. I must have turned out many thousands. But there were other implements made there, not only ploughs, cultivators, horse-rakes, but different machinery for land-work made specially to suit the foreign soils. But the noted plough for Suffolk was the Y.L.: there was a big demand for that, for work on the farms and for ploughing matches.

'The R.N.E. 4 was a favourite plough, too (it was named after a plough that the firm won a gold medal with at the Royal Show held in Newcastle) and I recollect one of these ploughs coming back to the shop for adjustment. The ploughman who had been using it had found it not quite to his liking so he had packed a ha'penny in between the breast and the share. When it came back to the shop I found the coin and I've kept it ever since.

'Ransome's used to keep a ploughman at the works and teams of horses specially to demonstrate their ploughs. These ploughmen competed at *drawing* or ploughing matches. I used to work with these men, and sometimes they'd bring back their plough with new ideas; and I'd make the alterations for them. Then they'd go away again as they were stationed in various parts of the country showing out these ploughs and getting orders. It was a great pleasure to me to go out into the field with one of these ploughmen and see him handling a plough that I'd made.

'I worked in Ransome's for nearly sixty years and there was a big difference when I finished from the time I started. At that time we were working from six in the morning till half-past five at night. That is to say, we had our breakfast in the shop. And a good many times I myself used to take a herring and cook that on the forge. Several of my mates used to gather round the forge and cook their breakfast and eat it together. We had a hot breakfast and we brewed up our own tea on the forge. There was no tea coming round the shops at that time o' day: we made our own.

'It was a six day week at that time. Our day-rate was 16s a week; a charge hand got half a crown more. If you were on piece-work you were allowed to earn up to a time and a quarter. But you had to keep your fingers going to do that.'

SOURCES AND BOOKS FOR FURTHER READING

GAIUS CARLEY. *The Memoirs of a Sussex Blacksmith*. Edited by Francis Steer. Moore and Tillyer, 1963
GARY HOGG. *Hammer and Tongs*. Hutchinson, 1964
The Pattern Under the Plough (Chapter 17)

14

The Miller and the Millwright

Under the old farming the mill was an essential part of the economy of the village in a corn-growing area like East Anglia. Most East Anglian villages had a working windmill up to the beginning of this century, and many mills continued to grind corn until recent years. Very few do this now; although there are a number of mills to be seen, occasionally even with their sails turning, their stones rarely grind corn. These mills have been preserved either by the Ministry of Works (Saxtead Green post-mill in Suffolk is an example) or by local effort as a kind of museum or nostalgic landmark in the countryside.

From near my present home I can see the post-mill which served the next village of Framsden for a century or so up to 1936. It stands on a hill, and the mill and its environs are a fitting reminder of the organization of the village before the recent changes. It is being restored at the present time (1967). But Framsden had a mill before the Domesday Survey of 1086; the site of this was on the low ground near the stream as this mill was driven by water. Five years ago a farmer discovered, in the field a mile or so on the other side of the windmill, an object that had earlier links. It was a piece of a Romano-British quern, an ancient device for grinding corn by hand.

Although the principle of the water-mill was known to the Romans they do not appear to have introduced it into Britain.

142

As far as we know, it was first used in these islands during the eighth century. But by the time of the Domesday Survey there were between five and six thousand water-mills in England. It was once believed that the windmill was an Eastern discovery brought back here by the Crusaders; but Lynn White, an American scholar, has got together evidence to show that the principle of the windmill was probably discovered independently in Europe. It is first mentioned in twelfth-century documents and it must have spread very quickly. Yet even after the setting up of countless water-mills and windmills the hand-mill or quern continued in use all over the country.

The reason was this: when the manorial lord built a mill he argued that since he had spent so much on such a costly improvement he was entitled to a proportionate return. Therefore all the people on his manor must take their corn to be ground at his new mill. Eventually the lord claimed the sole right to grind corn in the district under his jurisdiction. In fact he had a monopoly. He farmed his mill out to the miller and empowered him to keep back some of the villagers' corn or flour in payment for the milling. It was natural for many of the villagers to feel that they could well forego the benefits of modern improvements if they were to be bought at such a cost; and they continued to grind their corn at home on their querns. To combat this the manorial lord made the querns illegal; and whenever they were detected in any of the houses on the desmesne they were seized and broken up. It is likely therefore that many querns that have been discovered in a partial state were not broken by the plough but by some manorial officer defending his lord's monopoly. As Marc Bloch tells us in his *French Rural History*, there was a similar monopoly in France; and there, too, as in England this monopoly often embraced oven as well as mill. So when the peasant had paid to have his corn ground in the lord's mill he had the further privilege of paying to have his bread baked in the seigniorial oven.

It is not surprising, for this reason, that the miller ever since this time has had a very bad reputation. For it is natural for men to hate the instrument of a bad policy even more than the policy itself. Yet the miller down the ages has made his own peculiar contribution to the low esteem in which he was held. Chaucer's prototype, the Miller of Trumpington, was such a well-trained rogue that he could distinguish between the various degrees of filching; and he could steal as occasion served him, either 'courteously' or right 'outrageously'. And Chaucer's portrait of the miller has probably done as much as the hated medieval monopoly to give the miller a black mark. Even within living memory the following saying was often quoted: 'If you find an honest miller you'll know him by the tuft of hair growing in the palm of his hand.' But to do the miller justice he could with almost equal truth reply: 'Yes, maybe. But it takes the eye of an honest man to see it.'

A story from West Suffolk, told by George Jolly of Hargrave, points out that a miller was dependent on the wind, a chancy element; and it suggests that his nervousness to make full use of it laid him open to the charge of being grasping: A miller, not far from Bury St Edmunds, was in the habit of getting out of bed if the wind rose sufficiently during the night for him to grind his corn. And he expected his apprentice who lived quite near the mill to do the same. The lad did not think very much of this practice; and one night after being awakened by a rising wind he put his head under the pillow and went back to sleep again. Next morning he got the reception he expected from the miller:

'Boy! Where did you get to last night? It was a rare wind for grinding some of the corn.'

'That it was,' the boy agreed. 'But you should ha' bagged some on it up, Maaster. Then we should have had plenty on it to do the grinding today.'

All this gives the negative side of the miller's character. But a very different portrait of a miller is to be found in Appendix Two.

Today the mill 'sails' are wooden vanes whose angle can be adjusted from inside the mill. But not so long ago they were

30. Miller's Wagon

actually sails and had to be put up and taken down like the
sails of a ship. To enable the miller to do this more easily the
arms or stocks swept to within a couple of feet of the ground.
This can be seen clearly in the medieval illustrations of post-
mills which originally rested on a kind of wooden tripod. The
post-mill at Bourne in Cambridgeshire is a good example of the
early form. Later most post-mills were supported by a round
house made of bricks; and the *buck* or body of the mill raised
so that the arms did not sweep as near to the ground. Although
the low position of the buck was convenient in the days of the
sail, it was also very dangerous. A very old—and tall—story
illustrates this: a pedlar called at a mill and tied up his donkey
outside. When he emerged he found that his donkey had been
translated like Bottom—but up aloft.

The mill sails were a prominent feature of the village scene,
but sometimes they proved useful in a special way. Edmund
Samuel Webster (1854–1939) of Framsden mill, had a son
Samuel Webster (1877–1958) who owned the mill at Debenham
a few miles away. Father and son got so used to observing
each other's mill sails during the course of the day that they
developed a simple method of signalling. But in some parts of
Britain, notably in Sussex, signalling by means of mill sails
reached a more sophisticated level. In Sussex a miller was in

league with smugglers, and he allowed his mill to be used as a store-house for smuggled goods. By setting his sails at a certain position, for example a St Andrew's Cross, he could warn smugglers not to land their cargo whenever there were revenue officers about. These picturesque, turning mill sails were a delight to children; and this is borne out by Mrs Celia Jay of Blaxhall. When she was a child in the adjoining village of Tunstall, nearly eighty years ago, she and her companions used to chant the following rhyme as they watched the turning sails:

> *Father, mother, sister, brother:*
> *All go round but can't catch each other.*

It is worth pointing out that a visit to an old mill is given added interest by a search for *graffiti*. They are sometimes relevant to the mill's history. For instance, Edmund Samuel Webster of Framsden mill was apprenticed at Aythorp Roding post-mill in Essex, and his name can still be seen carved on the post.

The millwright was responsible for the upkeep and proper working of the mill. He was a skilled craftsman in both wood and metal; and although most practised millers *dressed* their own stones, dressing the grinding-stones of the mill to keep them in a condition to grind the corn efficiently was often done by the millwright. Jesse Wightman (born 1907 at Brandeston) was apprenticed to the miller at Saxtead Green. He learned his millwrighting from two millwrights who were once at Whitmore's the famous milling engineers from Wickham Market. The Saxtead post-mill still stands; and a few years ago Jesse Wightman restored it for the Ministry of Works. It is reputed to be the finest mill of its type in the country.

Stone-dressing involved deepening the *furrows* and cracking the *lands* of the grinding stones. The implement used for this was called a *bill-and-thrift*. The bill was made of high quality steel which had to be well-tempered to cut the almost diamond-hard stones. At one time Jesse Wightman had over fifty sets of millstones to dress. Some he dressed once a year; others about once a month, depending upon the amount of use the stones had. In later years many of the stones belonged to farmers who set up small motor-driven mills in their barns or outhouses to grind provender for their stock. But the roller mills and then the high speed grinder or hammer mills put the stone mills out of business. This process of displacement quickened up after the end of the Second World War; and by May 1962—as Jesse Wightman estimated—'all the old stone mills were practically gone'. He said at that time:

'I'm thinking of selling my holding and getting rid of some of my millwright's tools and taking another job. There are no more stones left to do.'

Shortly afterwards he left Saxtead and went to live in Chelmsford where he found constant work in local roller mills. Before he left Suffolk he gave me an account of how he dressed millstones; and as we walked out of his house on one of my visits he pointed out a doorstep made from a one-piece millstone. It had belonged to his great-grandfather:

'This is a *culling-stone*. It comes from Cologne in Germany. There aren't many of these stones about now. Millstones were usually made of French burr, and occasionally of millstone grit from Derbyshire. [This stone is one of the lower strata in the coal-measures in Britain; and miners knew that once they had reached the millstone grit the coal seams were worked out. In the South Wales coalfield millstone grit was known as the *farewell rock*.]

'The French stone is transported in sections called *burrs*, and the millwright has to cement them together and then bind the whole stone by a circular metal band or tyre in the same way as the wheelwright binds the wagon-wheel. But there's one important difference: the wheelwright cuts his metal tyre a certain amount shorter than the circumference of the wheel, so when the tyre cools after being placed on the wheel red-hot it would contract powerfully and tighten up all the joints in the felloes, spokes and nave. This kind of contraction would not apply to a stone so I cut the band to the exact circumference of the stone. I find this with a device I made myself, as I do

most of my tools. It's called a *traveller*. As you can see, it's a
metal wheel. I roll this round the stone and count the revolu-
tions. (It has a nick on the edge of the metal and I know exactly
when it's made one revolution.) I then roll the traveller along
a straight piece of tyre metal and get the exact length. [This
device works on the same principle as the measuring wheel
used by the old road surveyors—a trundle wheel or way-
wiser.]

'The first job after tyring is to *prove* the stone. This is sometimes called *flooring* or *levelling*. You have to be sure first of all
that before you use the stone it is absolutely flat. For this you
use a laminated piece of wood called a *millstaff*. But before you
do this the millstaff has itself to be proved. This is done on a
level slab of slate like a big oil-stone. It's called the *proof*. I
smear the proof over lightly with oil, then I run the millstaff
over it. The oil shows up those parts of the wooden staff that
are not true. These I scrape down with a piece of glass until
the staff is perfectly level. I then cover it with a solution of
tiver or scalded soot and run it over the stone. After the staff
has been on the stone any high places now appear black from
the soot. I dress these down until they're level with the rest of
the stone which I now rub down with a small burr rubber.

'The next job is to mark out the stone. But first of all, I'll
give you some idea of what a finished stone is like. It has a
number of channels cut into it, running from the centre or
eye of the stone to the circumference or *skirt*. These channels
are called the *furrows*; and, I suppose to keep up the similarity
to a ploughed field, the part of the stone between the furrows
is called the *land*. As the runner, the upper millstone, revolves
the corn is ground between it and the bed stone; and the corn
works out along the furrows until it emerges as meal or flour
at the skirt.

'For marking out a stone you need a *land spline* and a *furrow
spline*, pieces of flat wood the exact size that you want your
furrows to be. With one kind of *dress* these were $1\frac{7}{8}$ ins and
$1\frac{1}{8}$ ins wide respectively. I lay the furrow spline on the stone

and mark round its edge with a trimmed duck-feather dipped in a solution of soot and water (I always use a duck's or a goose's feather. An old stone man once told me that these were the best kind; and I believe he was right). Then I place the land spline, which is the wider of the two, alongside the furrow and the land is marked out in the same way. You repeat this method until you have marked right round the stone.

'One method of marking out and cutting the furrows is known as *harping* because each group of furrows that make up a *harp* or *quarter* of the dressed stone takes the shape of the strings of a harp. The *master* furrow is the first and longest; the *journeyman*, a slightly shorter one, comes next; the *apprentice*, shorter still, is next; and last of all the *butterfly*, which is the shortest. Usually the millwright makes nine or ten quarters or harp arrangements to his stone. But sometimes, according to the diameter of the stone, he will design it to have only three furrows in each group, and then the stone will have eleven or twelve quarters. The 'fly furrow is left out.

'The marking out is not as simple as it seems. For each furrow is not marked directly along the radius of the stone but slightly off centre. That is, the furrow does not follow the true radius but is marked from the skirt to a point *behind* the centre of the stone. This amount of difference between the furrow and the radius is called the *drift*. The amount of drift is proportionate to the diameter of the stone, and is normally in the region of an inch to every foot for a stone used to grind provender for cattle. For grinding wheat the drift is about half this amount.

'This is the *harp dress*. But there is another method, called the *sickle dress* which has a curved furrow (hence the name) narrow at the eye but broadening out as it reaches the skirt. There would be about 36 furrows in the sickle dress to a four-foot diameter stone.

'After the furrows have been cut the next job is *cracking* or *chasing* the lands. To do this I make regular indentations in

31. Mill-bill and thrift

each land with the same tool as I used to make the furrows—
the *mill-bill*. Here you see mine. It's a kind of steel pick or bill
mounted in a *thrift* or handle, made of wych-elm or some
other suitable wood. I made this one in 1936 and I've dressed
hundreds of stones with it. You can get an idea how many by
feeling this indentation in the thrift. It was made by my thumb
and it's worn as smooth as satin. The lines or scorings I make
on the land are about $\frac{1}{8}$ inch apart for grist or provender work
and about $\frac{1}{16}$ inch to make meal for human consumption.'

This dressing of the stones has given the miller and the
millwright tell-tale marks. They are on the back of his left
hand, and to look at they are not unlike the blue scars of the
coal miner. They are caused by small pieces of steel flying off
the bill and entering the skin as he chips away at the stone.
Around the mill-bill has gathered a great amount of mystery,
probably because the job of sharpening and tempering a bill
to cut the nearly diamond-hard stone is a very skilled one
which not every smith can do. A bill is made from a piece of
silver; or high quality carbon-steel. The secret was supposed to
be in the tempering process to make it ultra-hard. Jesse
Wightman said:

'I knew one man who was good at tempering bills: he
reckoned the magnetic pole had something to do with it, and
he always stood facing south as he was doing the job. But I
myself don't believe there's any secret or mystery about it at
all. It's just the know-how. Only many people believed there's
a secret to it. Some used spirits of hartshorn and sal-ammoniac

as a tempering solution. Others used a pound of borax to a gallon of hard water. Others again used coarse salt in solution. I knew a blacksmith at Harleston Green, Shelland, who used whale oil for tempering mill-bills, the same oil as he used for cart-springs. These solutions keep the atmosphere away from the hot steel, maybe, and give it some kind of sealing—but I'm doubtful. I believe it's just the technique, knowing for just how long to heat the steel, and being able to judge from the colour and so on the exact moment to dip the bill into the tempering vat. You could do it—Hector Moore, a friend of mine proved it—if you tempered in ordinary tap-water.'

To prove his point the millwright told me the story of a farmer who coveted what he thought was the secret of a blacksmith who was renowned for his well-tempered mill-bills. One day he went to the smith to settle up an account; while the smith had gone into the house to get him change, the farmer took a bottle out of his pocket and filled it with liquid from the tempering vat. He took the liquid to the chemist and paid a lot of money to have it analysed. The analysis showed that the water contained nothing but iron rust.

Jesse Wightman has a remarkable memory for anything connected with his craft. He knows the history of most mills in East Anglia, even some of the mills that were flourishing during the last century, as he had listened since he was a boy to the tales the older millers had told him. For instance, once during a talk with him I happened to mention that there was a mill—long since burnt down—in a Suffolk village where I used to live. This was Dyke's Mill, Blaxhall. He knew the exact date (1883) when it was destroyed, adding that it was said to be the largest post-mill in Suffolk, carrying four pairs of stones. In this connection I asked him why so many mills had been burnt down:

'You know that when a mill is turning, the stones have to be fed with corn all the time. If the runner stone revolves on the bed stone with nothing in between to grind there's soon trouble because the stones get hot and sparks fly out; and there

The Miller and the Millwright

is no lack in a mill of something to catch fire very quickly. That's the reason a mill has a warning bell which tells the miller that the hopper is no longer feeding corn to the stones. Many fires started this way; but many, too, were caused by the over-heating of the sail-neck bearing. Occasionally the sails ran away during a storm and there was a fire before grain could be fed to the stones or any action could be taken. But sometimes there was another reason for a fire. When there was the change-over from windmills to steam driven mills and later to oil, many of the old windmills couldn't compete. Somehow or other a convenient fire was reckoned to be arranged.'

SOURCES AND BOOKS FOR FURTHER READING

REX WAILES. *The English Windmill*. Routledge, 1954

R. THURSTON HOPKINS. *Old Water Mills and Wind Mills*. Allen, 1930

LYNN WHITE, JR. *Medieval Technology and Social Change*. Oxford University Press, 1962

MARC BLOCH. *French Rural History*. Routledge, 1966

NEWCOMEN SOCIETY. *Transactions*. Vols. XXII and XXIII (1941–3)

The Pattern Under the Plough (Chapter 17)

15

Conclusion

The miller and the millwright, the harness-maker and the tailor show how the old village community was dovetailed together by the nature of the work. For all the trades depended chiefly upon arable farming, the basic occupation of East Anglia. This feeling of a living unity in the village existed because the majority of its inhabitants were bound together directly or indirectly by the work. They depended upon farming; and what is more, on farming as it had been carried on for centuries with animal power and man power as its motive force. When the introduction of the internal combustion engine changed this, and made man and animal power less essential on the farm and brought the village nearer to the town, the old rural organization quickly fell away and the atmosphere in the village changed drastically within a couple of generations.

This, however, did not happen dramatically: it was the accelerated part of a movement that had started slowly in the last century. The threshing machine had long been invented; steam power had already been used in farming, but without changing its nature to any extent; the grass-cutter (adapted to form one of the first corn-reapers), the sail-reaper and the reaper-binder had all made their impact on the old ways of arable farming in the region. But the motor-engine, as a new, mobile and adaptable means of power and an annihilator of distance, was without doubt the chief agent in the change. And to say that farming was the last sector of our economy to feel the full impact of the Industrial Revolution is a fair—even if oversimplified—summary of what happened.

To imply that the old village, that has been displaced by the coming of full mechanization and the modern methods of farming, formed an organic unit is not to sentimentalize it. The organism was in fact far from being healthy. There was intense poverty in it, especially during some periods, and there were the tensions that were inevitable where the old system of dependence on master or squire had retained its force long after it had lost its relevance and many of its benefits. But the conditions of farming in a largely self-sufficient community, where needs could be satisfied without moving out of the village, made for at least a formal unity in the rural group. Framsden mill and its environs will illustrate what I mean about the compactness and self-sufficiency of the rural villages in East Anglia. Stanley Ablett (born 1895), the present owner of the mill and the mill-yard with its complex of buildings, recalled the scene when the mill was in full production:

'Over there on the other side of the yard was the blacksmith's shop with the wheelwright and carpenter's shop next to it. In the cottage on the other side of the stables lived the village shoe-maker. Then in Hill House, just outside the mill, where Mr Besley now lives, there was a grocer's shop kept by a Mr Flick who was also the village carrier, taking goods to and from Ipswich. In Hill House, too, a tailor used to work. That building in the corner housed the old portable steam-engine that Mr Webster the miller later bought: he used to grind the corn there when there was no wind. Later still he got an oil-engine; and people at that time could buy both coal and oil from the miller.'

Most of the village tradesmen were, therefore, within hailing distance of one another; and although this compactness un-doubtedly made Framsden an exception, it was the condition that most villages tended to. Transport to the town was difficult and made for self-sufficiency and reliance on village resources. There was only one form of public transport, the carrier's horse and cart that went once or twice a week to the town, and even then with little room or encouragement for passengers. What remained for most villagers was: 'The Hobnail Express', as Sam Friend put it, 'Shanks's Pony: stay home or walk twelve miles to Ipswich and perhaps spend the night on Mother Greenfield's pillow on the way back.'

To sum up: most of the villages in East Anglia, whether ancient or comparatively modern, were communities organized for a particular work. That work has always and chiefly been arable farming, except for the periods mentioned when sheep and wool, and cattle were in the ascendant. The revolution in farming during the last half-century by changing the character of the work also changed rural society. In addition, the easy access to the town made possible by the motor engine hastened this change because it enabled displaced or dissatisfied farm-workers to escape change's worst consequences by getting employment in the town. Yet the village itself could not escape change, even where the displaced workers continued to live in it. For it had ceased to become their working-place and instead became chiefly a place where they slept. Accordingly social life has tended to drain out of the village, and much of rural planning during recent years has been an active attempt to replace it.

It was suggested at the beginning that a history of farming in East Anglia has relevance to the present problems raised by a quickly changing rural society. This is implicit in the technique of going to the living community for historical evidence and of taking a wide view of the historical scene. By doing this one cannot escape contemporary happenings and the feeling that something like this has happened before. An example is the place of the small farmer in the new, evolving economy of today. Is there a future for him? Or are we to be reconciled to his disappearance, attributing it to something that was as inevitable as a thunderstorm and writing him off as one of

Conclusion

history's casualties exactly as society did the small farmer who was displaced by the enclosure movements which accelerated their pace roughly 200 years ago?

Now what is happening to the small farmer today bears a striking resemblance to a similar process that occurred centuries ago. This was the introduction of a new and comparatively sophisticated plough which helped to change not only farming but the whole social structure. This plough was, of course, the *carruca*, the heavy plough that the Saxons used to bring the rich clay lands of England under corn. The carruca was an expensive piece of farm gear because it contained—in share, coulter, hake and possibly wheel—a lot of iron, an expensive metal at that time; and it needed six or even eight oxen to draw it on heavy clay. It was not possible for a small farmer to own and use the carruca as his forefathers had used the *ard*, drawn by one, or at the most, two oxen. Therefore ownership *had* to be in common: one man owned the plough itself, for instance, another the coulter, share and hake; and perhaps six men each owned an ox. The land, therefore, when it was being prepared for winter corn, was ploughed in strips so that each part-owner of the plough-unit could get in a half-acre or so of seed-corn after an early autumn ploughing before the coming of the bad weather. Co-operation in the open-field, or communal farming—to give it another name—was not a matter of choice but of stark necessity.

The individual small farmer is faced with a similar situation today. Farming techniques have developed so quickly that the latest equipment is well beyond his means. No small farmer in a farm of 70–100 acres can justify ownership of any of the modern machinery—like the combine harvester—which present-day farming structure has made a necessity. If he wants to remain a farmer he has only one course open to him, as at least one president of the National Farmers' Union has repeatedly warned: he can become a member of a group which shares both machinery, and buying and marketing facilities. Only in this way can he escape extinction. But this would be communal

156

or co-operative farming, in fact a return on a higher level to the structure of the Middle Ages. This is already symbolized by the cutting down of the hedges that has made many of the fields of East Anglia *open* at least in appearance if not in social ownership.

Appendix One

Here is a tenancy agreement between a landowner and a small farmer. It was drawn up at the beginning of the century before the modern changes in farming began. In this document the Earl of Ashburnham appears to have appropriated the Norfolk four course rotation for Suffolk, but it was essentially the same system as is clear from his prohibition: 'NOT to take from off the same lands two white strawed crops in succession without the intervention of a green or pulse crops . . .'

Summerlands are fallow land (see *The Horse in the Furrow*, pp. 128–9). The reader will notice that the old calendar is used in the dating: Michaelmas, October 11th,; Lady Day, April 6th. Most Suffolk farm tenancy agreements still have these old dates.

Dated   6th May   1903

The Right Honourable Bertram

Earl of Ashburnham

and

Mr X Y

Agreement by Way of Lease

AN AGREEMENT made this 6th day of May, One thousand nineteen hundred and three Between the Right Honourable Bertram Earl of Ashburnham of the one part and X Y farm labourer, on the other part—Whereby the said Earl of Ashburnham lets, and the said X Y agrees to take and hold of him as Tenant, All that messuage, farm and lands with the outbuildings **and**

appurtenances thereto belonging called 'A.B. Hall' situate in
the County of Suffolk, containing Forty one acres or there-
abouts for the term of one whole year from the Eleventh day
of October last and so on from year to year until one of the said
parties shall give the other twelve calendar months' previous
notice in writing to determine the same, at the yearly rental of
Twenty eight pounds sterling, payable half yearly on the Sixth
day of April and the Eleventh day of October in every year
and under subject to the following reservations, conditions,
stipulations, and Agreements (that is to say):

The Said Earl of Ashburnham doth hereby reserve to himself All gravel, sand, stone, a brick earth, and All timber and
other trees, and young saplings, with liberty of ingress and
regress into and from the said lands and premises or any part
thereof at all seasonable times for taking and carrying away
the said reserved matters and things and for viewing and seeing
to the repairs and condition of the buildings, lands, and
premises, and for all other reasonable purposes whatso-
ever.

And the said Earl of Ashburnham doth also reserve to
himself the right of shooting and sporting over and upon the
said farm and lands in case he shall at any time hereafter during
the continuance of the Tenancy hereby created think fit to
exercise such right either by himself, his friends, agents, servants or Lessees.

And the said X Y hereby agrees to pay the said yearly rent
of Twenty eight pounds sterling by equal half yearly payments
at the times and in the manner aforesaid, and additional rent
of Twenty pounds per acre as ascertained and liquidated
damages for breaking or converting into tillage any meadows
or pasture lands; a proportionate sum for a greater or less
quantity.

To Pay all rates, taxes, and other assessments upon the said
farm and lands and every part thereof (except tithe, land tax,
and quit rent, and Landlord's Income tax).

To pay one third of the Workmanship and Labour which

may be required in putting and keeping the Farm house and other buildings in good and tenantable repair.

To keep in repair the glass windows and the glazing thereof.

To find all gate irons and nails.

To pay one third of the Labour of repairing all gates, lifts, posts, pales, stiles, bars, being allowed enough timber, bricks, stone and lime for such repairs.

To find all wheat straw for thatching, gratis.

To cart the material and find beer for the workmen gratis.

To cultivate the lands according to the Four course shift of Suffolk husbandry with liberty for the Incoming tenant to come upon the said lands in the spring time and sow clover or other artificial grass seeds with the summerland crops of the last year, the sowing of which due notice shall be given to him.

To harrow in such grass seeds without any allowance.

Not to permit cattle to be turned on the lands sown with grass seeds (except hogs well ringled).

Not to take from off the same lands two white strawed crops in succession without the intervention of a green or pulse crop (except with written permission). Beans and Peas to be twice clean hoed or a clean summertilth.

To spread on the Lands and premises all the hay, stover, straw, turnips and other roots produced thereon (except the first crops of Artificial and natural grass that may be mowed in the last year which shall be taken by the Incoming tenant at a Valuation).

To stack and inbarn on the premises all the corn, grain and pulse produced thereon.

In the last year to leave all the straw, chaff and colder of that year's crop well preserved for the Incoming tenant on being paid for the threshing and dressing the corn, grain and pulse and having the same carried by him to any place not exceeding the distance to Ipswich in quantities of not less than twenty eight coombs at a time except the last load.

To spread on the Land all the muck, manure, and compost,

produced on the premises, the muck produced from last year's straw to be left in heaps for the Incoming tenant on being paid for the same at a Valuation.

To yield up possession on the determination of the tenancy.

To sweep the chimneys in the farm house twice every year.

Not to assign or underlet the said farm lands and premises or any part thereof.

Not to top any pollard trees nor cut alders of younger growth than eight years nor of older growth than twelve years.

No valuation to be allowed for alders nor for any other description of wood at the determination of the tenancy.

To have the use of the Barns and stackyards until the first day of May after determination of the tenancy; and at such determination to be paid for rates, and tillage of that year's summerlands, for the seed sowing and hoeing of turnips, and the hay and stover sowen feed, and much to be then left as aforesaid so much money as the same shall be valued to be worth by two indifferent and competent persons (one to be chosen by each party or their umpire).

IN WITNESS whereof the said parties hereto have hereinto interchangeably set their hands, the day and year first written above.

Witness   Ashburnham
                                          per Henry Lingwood
                                                  his agent.

A Valuation is mentioned in the above Agreement. This is the estimate made before a tenant moves out of a holding so that he can be compensated for the material he has left behind as well as for the work on land whose profit will accrue after he has left.

The following Valuation was made for Mr X Y prior to his taking A.B. farm, and the amount of the award was then payable to the outgoing tenant.

MICHAELMAS, *1902*

A.B. Hall, Suffolk

Mr H. Lingwood
to
Mr X Y

Award (Valuation)

Alfred Preston,
  Worlingworth and Ipswich

Valuers

P. C. N. Peddar,
Stowmarket.

	Valuation or Covenants
	From Mr Henry Lingwood to Mr X. Y. comprising
acres roods poles 9 0 0 more or less	*Fallows* The Tillage, Seed, Manure and Rates thereon Heap of Manure Two Stacks of Hay and Stover
Fixtures	*Keeping Room* Stove *Back House* Copper as fixed, Oven Lid *Outside* Stack Rick on Stone Piers
	The above were Viewed and Valued for the sum of Fifty Pounds four shillings
	By us:
£50 4 0 5 0 ½ Stamp	Alfred Preston P. C. N. Peddar
£50 9 0	

Appendix Two

The following tale about a Suffolk miller from Gosbeck was
told me by a Stonham Aspal man, W. H. Thurlow (born 1892).
He related the story with great feeling and confessed he was
greatly affected by the thought of the lost pony and the miller's
devotion to it. I wrote the story down more or less as he told
it to me. I did this for more than one reason: because I recognized its quality, because it is a kind of folk-tale in the making;
and because it does impart a little of the atmosphere of the
small Suffolk village before the recent changes came upon it. I
have called it

THE MILLER AND HIS PONY

If the people of Gosbeck had been asked who was the most
popular man in the village they would have answered without
thinking twice: George Southgate the miller. And they probably
would have added that his pony was just as popular as he was.
George Southgate was a big man by any standard. He was tall,
well over six feet; but he was so finely proportioned that to
look at him you wouldn't have thought he was above average
height. He had more strength than he knew and he could
throw a sack full of corn across the mill floor almost as easily
as if it had been a pillow. He was known much farther afield
than his own village; for his dealings were as straight as his
back and his kindness was as large as his hand.

Now George's pony was called Tom. There was nothing
remarkable about Tom, at least not to look at. He stood about

fourteen hands; more the size of a cob than a pony; but a pony they used to call him. He was a dark chestnut in colour and was a good-tempered and willing little worker. But Tom was a great favourite in the village because he was everyone's cheerful servant. For the miller always left the door of Tom's stable open; and if anyone wanted to borrow him—at any time of the day or night—they had only to go to his stable, harness him up and take him out. Both Tom and his master were willing, and no one had ever used him badly.

But just before Christmas (and the time I'm talking about was over sixty years ago, right at the beginning of the century) Tom was taken out of his stable one night and he was not returned the next morning. There was nothing unusual in this, and it caused the miller no worry. For often the pony had been away a whole night and a day, when the affairs of one of his neighbours had got into such a tangle that someone would have to go to Colchester or perhaps Norwich to sort them out.

When, however, Tom had not returned by dusk on the following day the miller decided to make some inquiries. He asked his wife whether Mr Marjoram had been over to see his sick mother at Bilderston. He had not; nor did Mrs Southgate know of anyone else who might have borrowed the pony.

George Southgate had a troubled and restless night; and he got up and went out to the stable before it was light. His two other horses were still there, but Tom's stall was empty; and he knew he couldn't keep down his fears any longer. Something had happened to Tom. Now the miller was a good man who thought well of his neighbours, and was slow to admit that anyone had robbed him. But after the pony had been missing for two days he decided to go for the police.

That Christmas was a bleak one for the miller and his family. The empty stall was like a big hole in the side of the house, reminding them all the time of their loss. The people of the village, too, missed Tom; and more than once a child's question: 'Tom hasn't come back yet, Mr Southgate?' kept the miller's loss as raw as any wound.

Shortly after Christmas he had a visit from the policeman who'd had a report that a pony very much like Tom had been seen in Essex. Someone in the town of Chelmsford had noticed him, tied to another horse and being led on the way towards London. When this became known, Herbert Pipe, the miller's friend, told him:

'It's a bad business, George. Tom's up in the London smoke long afore this, you may depend. And I reckon they'll have a rare job of finding him up there. That they will.'

The miller said nothing in reply to this; but some time later an incident showed very clearly what was in his mind. One of his men, looking for a place to store some of the corn that was coming in after the winter threshing, had taken a few sacks and had placed them in Tom's empty stall. As soon as he got to know about this the miller ordered the sacks to be removed and the stall to be kept exactly as it used to be when the pony was out on one of his errands.

'You're not expecting on Tom back, are you, Master?' one of the men had asked. 'Or maybe you're thinking of getting another pony?'

But the miller refused to talk about the pony to anyone. And the people in the village began to shake their heads and say that it was the first time in his life that George Southgate had been stubborn about anything. The pony had gone. It was no use trying to escape that. Though everybody was sorry to lose Tom, because they'd never see another pony like him again.

'Facts are facts,' Hub Pipe had said, though not in the miller's hearing; 'once the pony's got up there in the Smoke you just can't imagine what's happened to him. They're up to all manner of tricks up there. They'd alter him in no time! Poor old Tom might have stripes and be a zebra in the Zoo for all we know about him. It's no use George a-pining and a-sorrowing and expecting on him back. He's got as much chance o' finding him now as I got of spending that half-sovereign I lost out o' my weskit pocket that time I was a-ploughing down at Backhouse Close.'

Yet the miller was sure he would find his pony again. And in the months that followed his disappearance he acted according to a definite plan. He went out of the village nearly every week to a show or a horse-fair; and he soon became well known wherever horses were brought together. His big, tall figure, open face, and his fair hair and side-whiskers made him stand out in any crowd. But when they knew his purpose most people passed him by—even those who knew him.

But the miller heard nothing of Tom during the whole of his wanderings; and on Christmas Eve, a year after Tom was stolen, his wife told him:

'You're driving yourself off your balance, George, a-worrying about the pony. Tom will never come back now; and the sooner you believe that, the better it will be for all of us.'

But George shook his head and talked about something else whenever his wife tried to reason with him.

The following summer he again travelled all over the Eastern Counties but found no clue. Then he changed his tactics. He took to visiting the inns along the main roads in his own county of Suffolk. He'd call at an inn and order a glass of beer; he'd sip it for a while and then he'd slip out to the back where he'd examine all the horses that happened to be in the stables.

By this time the people of Gosbeck began to wonder whether George Southgate was seeing things in their proper order; and they nodded at one another when they met him in some strange inn, sitting by himself in the bar waiting his chance to look over the stables. But the people of Gosbeck were wrong. For it was in this way that George Southgate found his pony and brought him home to the village again.

It was almost two years after Tom had been stolen. One morning the miller got up rather earlier than usual and said to his wife:

'You'll take charge of the mill for me today, gel? I've got a mind to go up to Norwich.'

'To Norwich! Whatever are you going to do in Norwich?'

'I don't rightly know,' George answered as he put on his broad-cloth jacket. 'But I'll take good care of myself and I'll see you some time afore midnight.'

And his wife, knowing that there would be no point in arguing with him, packed him a few sandwiches in a white linen cloth, and saw him start off to walk to the 'Rose' inn at Crowfield where he intended getting a lift with the carrier.

As soon as he reached Norwich George Southgate made straight for an inn that lay not far from the foot of the Castle. By this time he had got himself a reputation. He had become known as 'the mad miller who's allus a-looking for his pony'. But the owner of this particular inn happened to be an acquaintance, and George asked him:

'Do you mind if I have a look at your stables, Robert?' The landlord nodded and pointed to a side-door. George Southgate went out, leaving his beer hardly touched on a table.

The stables were in the inn-yard, four stalls on each side. The miller went straight to the first stall on the right without hesitating. He leaned over the locked half-hatch door and stared at the pony that was standing inside, dismal and unmoving. He could see that it had been neglected. Its coat had felt neither the brush nor the curry-comb for weeks: he looked dispirited and his head was almost as low as the ground. The miller gripped the rough edge of the half-door. Then he whispered hoarsely, 'Tom!' The pony raised his head slowly, turning a dull eye towards the miller. 'Tom!' he repeated more loudly. The pony now raised his head a little higher; and immediately he shuffled restlessly about the stall as though the miller had touched something deep inside him.

In a couple of seconds George Southgate had vaulted over the door and was standing inside the stall stroking the pony's neck; and as he stirred and began to show some life, George shouted in his excitement:

'Tom! Tom! And they told me I should never find you.'

When some of his feeling had died down he stepped back

and looked at the pony again: 'But what if it isn't Tom, after all,' he thought. His doubts made him cold. This pony, this pony so rough and neglected could never be his. Then he remembered the old trick he had once taught him. If the pony now recalled it there could be no doubting that it was Tom. The miller stood back and slowly put his right hand into the deep pocket of his jacket. Without hesitation the pony nuzzled his head against the miller's arm and expertly lifted his hand out of his pocket. Then he searched the miller's hand for the sugar he knew he would always find in it. And the sugar was there in George Southgate's hand—so sure was he that at the last he would find his pony.

He now gripped the pony's mane with his huge hand and said: 'Tom, it's you right enough. But what a terrible sight they've made on you.'

When he recovered he climbed back over the door, crossed the yard and went straight to the bar of the inn. There were three men there now, and the landlord said pleasantly:

'I've kept your beer for you, George. You better drink it up afore you lose it.'

'Thank you, Robert,' the miller answered quietly; and he finished the drink in one draught and placed the empty glass back on the counter.

'I'll trouble you, Robert, for the key to that first stall on the right in your stables.'

For a moment the landlord looked at him blankly, and his alarm showed in his face:

'But I'm holding, I'm holding it. That pony belongs to three customers, George.'

'I want that key, Robert,' the miller repeated, 'and I want it now. The pony in that stall is a stolen one.'

The landlord, seeing that it would now be impossible to reason with the miller, shrugged his shoulders, took down a key that was hanging from a shelf behind him and handed it over the counter.

'What are you going to do with the pony, George?'

'I know right well what I'm a-going to do with the pony, Robert. But that's not the only job that wants doing. You'd better come out along with me.'

The landlord and the three men in the bar followed the miller out to the stables and stood by as he opened the stall. As soon as the pony was out in the small yard he threw up his head, neighed and pushed himself gently against his master who walked him round and round in his excitement.

'Now, whose pony is he?' he shouted. 'You see for yourself, Robert. It's Tom. It's Tom. And show me the man who'll deny it.'

The three men who were farmers, in town for the market, knew the miller by repute and were immediately sympathetic.

'Look at him,' George Southgate said, stopping the pony in front of them. 'They've hogged his mane and docked his tail and nearly ruined him into the bargain. But they couldn't disguise him from me!'

The landlord, quite sure now in his own mind that the pony did in fact belong to the miller, said that they'd better send for the police. Three 'townies', chaps from London way, had left the pony there that morning. But George Southgate disagreed. If once the police were seen coming to the inn, the supposed owners might get wind of it and they would certainly not come back for the pony. He added:

'And I'd dearly like to have a word with those London chaps before me and Tom go home to Gosbeck.'

So it was decided that they should lock Tom in his stall once more, and that the landlord should hang the key back in the bar as if nothing had happened. The miller was to wait outside the stall ready to meet the men when they returned.

'But you can't just wait in the yard there by yourself, Mr Southgate,' one of the farmers said to George. 'Like as not they'll give you a leathering.'

'Leave 'em to me,' the miller said quietly. 'I reckon it's not me who'll get the leathering.'

The three farmers, however, were by this time nearly as

anxious to catch the thieves as the miller; and they decided to
hide in the stall adjoining Tom's, as it happened by chance
to be vacant. It was early afternoon when the men returned to
collect the pony. George Southgate knew they had arrived
even before they had entered the yard. The back window of
the inn had opened suddenly—a signal pre-arranged with the
landlord; and George was ready for them when they came out.
The three men wore long black jackets and coloured handker-
chiefs round their necks. The miller recognized them as 'horse-
sharpers': it was written plainly all over them. The oldest of
the men held the key; and seeing the miller standing firmly
before the stall he stopped and said abruptly:

'You'll catch cold standing out here, mate. We'll trouble you
to get out of the way. We've come for the pony.'

George Southgate looked at them for a moment before
replying. Then he said in his deep voice:

'You're not taking this pony out of here. I can tell you that.
This pony was stolen, and you're now going to tell me how
you came by him.'

The man with the key glanced quickly round the yard;
nodded briefly to his companions and advanced towards the
miller. The smallest of the men made a move to get behind him,
but the miller retreated until he felt the door firmly at his back.
The three continued to move cautiously towards him. Then,
without a previous sign of what he was about to do, the
oldest of the three men aimed a vicious kick into the miller's
stomach. But the miller was ready for him; and bending
almost double and at the same time moving quickly to one
side, he grasped the man's leg tightly by the ankle. Then just
as he was about to overbalance he caught his long jacket, and
swinging him off his feet he flung him like a sack of chaff right
across the yard to the stalls opposite. Luckily there was a pile
of straw there to break his fall;otherwise it would have been
fatal. The two other men, who had been completely surprised
by the miller's quickness, now came in again. The small man
suddenly ducked and tried to grasp his legs to bring him to the

ground. But as he came in the miller hit him with a flat hand and he went down senseless on to the cobbles. The third man he caught by the loose clothes on his chest and hurled him right across the yard into the arms of the three farmers who were now coming out of the empty stall. Then he picked up the key and strode over and opened the door to Tom's stall.

George Southgate led Tom out of Norwich just as it was getting dusk. There had been many things to see to before he could take the pony away. The police had locked up the men, and they were soon recognized as horse-thieves with a reputation that extended far beyond the Eastern Counties. But in spite of the delay George arrived home, as he had promised his wife, well before midnight. Tom's stall was ready for him, even to the oats for his supper and the straw for his bedding. When he went upstairs and told his wife that he had found Tom, she wouldn't believe him. So he lighted the horn-lantern and took her down to the stable. She tried to speak to the pony but was not able to. Then the miller said kindly:

'Never mind, gel. Tom's home now. And he's the best Christmas box you and me could ever have been given. But do you get back to bed before the cold gets properly into you.'

The next day was the Eve of Christmas; and as soon as the news got round the village a stream of people—grown-ups as well as children—came to look at Tom standing in his stall. He was lost, and now he had been found. The prodigal had come home after a long wandering; and the miller and his wife were completely happy again. To the people of Gosbeck this in itself was like a miracle. That the miller should ever have found his pony again was beyond the bounds of ordinary understanding.

Hub Pipe stood by the miller watching the pony munching one of the tit-bits the children were continually bringing him. After a while he turned to him and said cheerfully:

'I reckon that now he's back you'll not be leaving the stable-door open like it was, George. You'll lock it up in case some unkind friend will take Tom on his travels again.'

The miller pondered this before replying. Then he said with gentle deliberation:

'No, Hub. This stable door will always be unlocked' and as he stroked the pony's neck he added: 'and if old Tom here had a tongue that could talk he'd say himself that he wouldn't like it to be otherwise.'

George Southgate was born in 1862 and died in 1946. Shortly after I wrote down this story I met Mrs May Gladwell. She is the only surviving member of George Southgate's own family: she was born in Gosbeck mill in 1886. She remembers 'Tom pony' very clearly, and she said:

'The story as related by Herbert Thurlow is true in all the essential details. But one thing is missing from the story as he told it. While my father was away on his wanderings looking for the pony, my mother had to look after the mill. And as there were six of us children—three boys and three girls—it was pretty hard on her sometimes.'

Mrs Wardley (born 1907), whose family has kept Crowfield 'Rose' for over seventy years, is George Southgate's grand-daughter. Herbert (*Hub*) Pipe, George's friend, was also her grandfather on her mother's side. She was too young to remember the theft of the pony, but she often heard her mother talk about it:

'I recollect her saying that on the day George Southgate went to Norwich to get his pony, as he said, he called here at "The Rose". When he told them where he was going they just laughed at him.'

Glossary

---

ard Primitive scratch plough

awns Beard at the end of grain-sheath of barley

back'us (*Backhouse*, or perhaps, *bakehouse*) Back kitchen of a farm-house. *B.-boy*, the boy who did the odd jobs there

bagging-hook (*-iron* or *bagger*) A tool once used for cutting corn. Still in use for cutting grass or hedges

bale Curved attachment to a scythe; used when cutting barley. See also *cradle*

barleysel The time of the barley or corn harvest

bay Division of timbered house or barn

beetle A mallet with heavy wooden head

billy-cock A felt hat with a high crown

brakes Bracken

brazier Container or pan for holding lighted charcoal

bush-drain Under drain in a field: bottom section of this stuffed with bushes

bush-harrow Primitive harrow made from a hawthorn b. weighted with a log

bushel Ancient wooden measure for corn; still in use

buttrice Blacksmith's tool, once used to cut the frog on a horse's hoof

cadows Jackdaws

carruca (or *caruca*) First true plough

cast Tinge of colour: 'The field has a different cast now'

cattle-beet Mangel-wurzels, a frequent root-crop 50 years ago

champion The open-field or open-field farmer

change-ringing The ringing of bells in a set, 'scientific' order

Glossary

clip To shear sheep; *a clip*, the shearing or the amount of wool shorn; *clippers*, shearers

colder Husks or short pieces of straw

comb (or *coomb*) A measure, equal to four bushels

communal farming Farming where many combine to till the land

cords Reins on horses when ploughing

coulter Knife or blade fixed in front of share on plough; *seed-c.* the hollow 'knife' down which seed runs into the soil from the hod or container of drill

cradle Attachment (usually of wood) to scythe when cutting wheat

crop-rotation Change or succession of crops on a given piece of land

crow-keeping Guarding land, sown with seeds, from crows and other birds

curry-comb Iron implement for rubbing down a horse

day-man (or *day-labourer*; cf *journeyman*) Farm hand paid by the day

demesne The lord of the manor's estate

devonshiring Paring land and then burning the vegetation

dibber (or *dibbler*) Heavy iron rod with blobbed end for making holes in soil to take seed

dock To cut short, e.g. a horse's tail or mane

drawing Furrow-drawing or ploughing

dress To clean corn of impurities

drill Machine for sowing corn in rows. *Drilling*, the process of using this

dropping Sowing seeds in holes made by dibbers

dutfin Medieval word for horse-bridle

enclosure Process of marking off land with fence or boundary, thus removing it from common use

fallow Land bearing no crop but left to recover from previous croppings

false-link Spare chain-link carried by ploughman in field

fill-horse see *thiller*

flag Turf, or turf turned over to form a furrow

Glossary

four-course shift System of crop-rotation evolved in Norfolk: 1st year, roots (cattle-beet, turnips, etc.); 2nd, barley; 3rd clover; 4th wheat

frog V-shaped horny, elastic pad in centre of horse-hoof

frolic Celebration or jollification

fye To clean (medieval word)

gang-master Man in charge of a field-gang of women and youths

gavel To rake up, usually barley

glove-money Payment to harvesters, originally to buy gloves to protect hands against thistles in corn

gove (or *goaf*) Corn in the mow, that is before it has been threshed

graffiti Drawings or carvings on wall, etc. *Sing. graffito*

grass-nail Attachment to help fix scythe blade to stick or handle

hake Hook attachment in front of plough, or in chimney

harrow A heavy frame with iron teeth, drawn over land to break up clods

harvest-lord Elected to take charge of harvest under the old farming; usually the farm foreman. *h. lady*, his deputy

havels Awns of barley

haysel Hay harvest

headlands (*Headlings* in East Anglian dialect) Strip of land near field boundary; left for convenience of turning plough

horkey Harvest celebration or frolic

horse-hoe Machine drawn by horse to weed between crop-rows

hounces Coloured worsted ornaments on a horse

hulver Holly (medieval word)

knacker Maker of harness for farm-horses; a horse-slaughterer

largesse Harvest gift, usually in form of money

locust-bean Fruit of the carob tree; once fed to farm animals

melton-cloth Broad c. for coating, from Melton in Leicestershire

middlings Coarser part of flour left after boulting or sieving

muck-crone Fork with bent tines used in dung-shifting

net'us Neat- or cattle-house

open-field Arable field farmed in common

overseer of highway Parish officer who was in charge of roads before these taken over by County Council *peason* Peas

plaiting Decorating a horse's tail or mane with bass

poke A bag

quern Ancient hand-mill for grinding corn

quit-rent Rent paid by tenants of a manor in lieu of the services they owed (a medieval survival)

ranter Copper jug or container

reaper-binder see *self-binder*

retting-pit For steeping flax or hemp in water in order to loosen fibres

rib-roll Land roller with corrugated surface

ringes Rows of growing plants, or the seed channel

rubbish Weeds

sail-reaper One of the early corn-reaping machines

scalled or *scolled* Burnt up (of field-crops)

scarify To stir the soil

scuppit Shovel or spade

seed- or *sid-lip* Hod for holding seed when broadcasting

self- or *reaper-binder* First machine to cut corn and bind it into sheaves at same time

several or in *severalty* Farming in s.; farming in separate individual holdings

spear-grass Quitch-, twitch- or couch-grass

spit A spade, hence depth of earth pierced by spade

spud Small, knife-like hoe for cutting out weeds

stetch or *stitch* Section of land in ploughing; cf. *ridge* or *land*

strike Strip of wood with straight edge for levelling a bushel of grain

summer-land Fallow land; *s. tilth*, the cultivating of this

swap-hook or *swab* A bagging-hook

swing-plough Plough without a wheel

thiller or *thill-* or *fill-horse* Horse between the shafts of a tumbril or cart

tie-beam Length of wood to tie or brace parts of a building together

tiller Shoot of a plant, such as wheat or barley

Glossary

tilt Canvas or tarpaulin cover
tine A fork-prong
tumbril Two-wheeled farm cart
weskit Waistcoat
worrell Iron ring at top of scythe-stick
yard Allotment or small piece of land

M

Index

Index

Under-draining, 27–30
Valuation, 161
Virgil, *The Georgics*, 47–48
Wales; grass-growing, 14, 45–46
Warren, C. Henry, 82
Weed-hook, 50
Western Iran (first corn grown), 17

Weston, Sir R., 23, 93
White, Lynn, Jr., 143
Whittlesford, 40–42, 110–12
Wilson-Fox, A., 58, 89, 102
Winnower (or *blower*), 90
Young, A., 33, 35, 100, 108